NEGLIGENCE!
AVERTING DISASTER
AT YOUR BUILDING

LESSONS LEARNED FROM
THE CHAMPLAIN TOWERS COLLAPSE

GREG BATISTA, PE

NEGLIGENCE! AVERTING DISASTER AT YOUR BUILDING:
LESSONS LEARNED FROM THE CHAMPLAIN TOWERS COLLAPSE
by Greg Batista, PE

ISBNs: 978-1-0880-3030-1 Trade Paperback
         978-1-0880-3037-0 Hardcover
         978-1-0880-3031-8 Ebook

Contents

Introduction

When I was in second grade, my mom bought me the toy that would change my life: Lincoln Logs. Before the age of Legos, there were Lincoln Logs. I realized that I wanted to grow up to build, create, and design from an early age. I loved making art and I also had a visual, three-dimensional mind.

While I am an engineer by trade, I have always been drawn to creative endeavors. I prefer to pass the time writing poetry, making music, and producing videos. These creative pursuits even took me to the extent of joining a traveling dance groups during my college years. Growing up, I gravitated toward architecture because it fuses the technical with aesthetics and creativity. I was devastated when I found out that I couldn't get into college for architecture, and my family could not afford to send me out of state for college. Where I grew up in Puerto Rico, there was just one architecture school, which accepted only about 15 students per year. I then decided to go for my second-best option: structural engineering.

In hindsight, that was the best outcome I could have hoped for since, as a structural engineer, I leverage my natural talents for math, the analytical, and computers. At the same time, I channel my creativity through other means. Today, I own a building with a studio for my creative projects and an office for my technical work.

During my last year of engineering school in 1991, I began working for Turner Construction Company, one of the largest construction companies globally at that time. The experience was incredible for me. At a relatively young age, I was "in the trenches" learning high-rise construction at a world-class level.

By my early 30s, I was at the top of my game in construction as a project manager on multiple high-rise projects in South Florida. Never mind that I barely slept and was caught in a constant state of stress from managing 300 to 400 people on a project. Still, I was good at the work and loved the challenge.

The thrill was not enough to keep me going much longer, and I was quickly burning out. I told myself I would start a structural engineering business instead. My construction buddies mocked me, saying I was moving on to a cushy desk job where I would sit around in air conditioning and draw "pretty pictures" all day. Construction folks typically think engineers have the most comfortable jobs since we work in air-conditioned offices while they're out in the field, cracking the whip in what many believe is one of the most high-stress jobs on earth.

I knew little about owning and operating a real-world engineering office. I had my college education, my license, and limited experience in actual design engineering, and that was about it.

"I'm going to open an engineering business anyway," I decided. Everyone thought I was crazy. However, most people know that the fundamental education in your career only comes from hands-on experience after you graduate. In my case, ignorance was most certainly bliss as I learned how to establish and run an engineering business the hard way. Fortunately, I was lucky enough to start my business when engineers were in high demand.

After two years, I had five employees. After three years, it was ten. Slowly but surely, I was growing. Most of our projects were engineering jobs where I performed the designing myself. So I taught myself to design (of course, with the help of some brilliant people) and learned all the codes so I could hire the right people and be in responsible charge of our projects. Our first five years were a period of intense learning. That was over 20 years ago.

Today, I have more than three decades of hands-on construction, design, and engineering experience. It's what sets me apart from everybody else. I often act as an expert witness in court cases involving engineering and construction mishaps. I've participated in over 100 cases in the past ten years. It's rare to have the knowledge and background in engineering and construction at the level I do.

Throughout my career, I've witnessed many unfortunate events, from jobsite accidents to hurricanes, sinkholes, and earthquakes, including the immediate aftermath of the Haiti earthquake of 2010 that claimed 200,000 lives. Every construction or engineering tragedy has lessons to be learned from it. My extensive hands-on experience performing thousands of inspections and working with hundreds of condominiums in South Florida gives me a unique vantage point to understand why the Champlain Towers tragedy occurred and to make real-world recommendations.

Before I ever decided to write this book, I developed the "Ask G. Batista" brand to help educate non-engineering folks about the intricacies of engineering and construction. The main goal is to allow people to make better decisions about taking care of the places where they live, work, vacation, and play. I've even written several books, which are available on my website www.askgbatista.com, to answer many of the questions most residents, owners, property managers, and real estate agents (and other non-engineering and construction types) have when they are thinking of undertaking maintenance, renovations, and repairs to their property.

I come from a family of teachers and my curiosity has driven all I have done in life. It led me to found and own an engineering and construction business at the tender age of 32. As someone who so highly values the learning process, I love sharing the knowledge I've gained. With this book, my goal is to help everyday people learn and understand why this tragedy occurred and how we can keep it from happening again through the lessons learned from the Champlain Towers. And, as aging structures continue to deteriorate in our country, it's become critical to broadcast these lessons to the broader public.

The nation's infrastructure and buildings are deteriorating and consistently receiving failing grades from top engineering and professional groups. Apart from bridges, roadways, water plants, and underground utilities, we have buildings where we live, play, shop, and work. The buildings where we live will be the primary focus of this book. Florida alone has more than 1.5 million residential condominiums, of which nearly half are at least 40 years old. For the past 30 years, I have devoted my life to engineering and repairing these existing structures.

Let this book serve as an initial non-technical education for everyday people, like many I speak to almost daily who don't understand how something like this could happen here in the United States in the 21st Century. Let this book also serve as a testament to the human spirit that strives to learn from past mistakes so that future generations can build better lives for themselves, their families, and the community at large. But most importantly, as a professional who feels that our industry has let down the people we have sworn to protect, let this book serve as a tribute to those that perished in this tragedy, with the hope that we will have the tenacity to find out exactly why this happened and the political will and courage to make the necessary rectifications.

Chapter I

Presenting the Problem

Throughout the years, I have come to rely on analogies to explain certain complex engineering and construction concepts to my clients. The following analogy is one of my favorites since it neatly expresses the intricacies of an inanimate object and brings home the idea of adequately maintaining and taking care of said object.

The structures we occupy are like a human body.

Condos, homes, industrial power plants, and office buildings are like human bodies. Human bodies have plumbing systems that allow water to enter to provide cleanliness and plumbing systems designed to get rid of waste. Buildings possess similar systems. Where human bodies have a nervous system, condominiums have electrical systems with receptacles, fire alarms, security cameras, and long strands of cabling connecting each one of these components.

Then you have the skin. The skin of a building is significant and protects the building, just as our skin protects us from diseases, foreign objects, and viruses. If a building doesn't have a robust and healthy skin, such as solid windows and doors, it will leak when there's rain or other inclement weather. And in a worst-case scenario, people's lives will be at risk in the event of a hurricane.

Just as our bones prevent us from plummeting to the ground like a blob, a building's structure is what keeps it standing. The similarities go on and on. We hope that our Creator endows us with the necessary genetics that will allow us to live a long and healthy life in much the same way that we hope that the engineers who design buildings do an excellent job ensuring that they adequately design their structures. Unfortunately, some buildings are not designed correctly and we must thus suffer the consequences of these errors. Similarly, as buildings age, we must care for them as we care for our slowly-deteriorating bodies.

Structural issues are not the only concern with buildings. For example, people can get electrocuted from electric issues in buildings because somebody didn't correctly design the system or simply didn't install a ground wire where it was supposed to go. Mechanical systems are also crucial in the same manner that our respiratory, immune, and circulatory systems work in our bodies to regulate our body's temperature and other indispensable functions.

For example, in July of 1976, a convention held at the Bellevue-Stratford Hotel in Philadelphia experienced an outbreak of Legionnaires' disease. There was something wrong with the hotel's air conditioning filtration system. As a result, the disease spread throughout the hotel, causing 182 cases of the illness and resulting in 29 deaths.

If we don't take care of our health, our bodies are more susceptible to breaking down. So we hopefully maintain practices meant to keep our bodies healthy for all the years to come with regular check-ups from our doctors, dentists, and therapists. The number one reason building maintenance is essential is for the health and safety of the people in those buildings. All building maintenance elements affect the safety of their residents. If you don't take care of those issues, tragedies like those at the

Champlain Towers or the Bellevue-Stratford Hotel will eventually occur.

Statistics

The United States infrastructure is on life support. Let me start with a couple of statistics. The Army Corps of Engineers and the ASCE (American Society of Civil Engineers) have given the United States an almost-failing grade concerning the general state of its infrastructure. Periodically, these entities provide a report card that depicts the condition and performance of American infrastructure in the familiar form of school grades. The ASCE reports that 70,000 bridges (or one out of every nine) bridges are "structurally deficient," which means that they need substantial repairs or need complete replacement. In Pittsburgh alone, 20% of the bridges have been deemed "structurally deficient" and approximately 300 bridges are added to that list every year in Pennsylvania. I could go on about the state of our roads, airports, and other structures that comprise our nation's infrastructure. At the root of this lingering problem is a lack of funding to perform the repairs—the money cannot be allocated faster than the repairs can be made. This speaks mostly to government dysfunction and the general lack of education and expediency at the highest levels.

Engineers like to say that people don't even think about it when infrastructure works. But most citizens immediately recognize it when your car is in traffic or hits a pothole, your water or electricity services fail, when a levee erodes, or when there is a structural failure.

In Florida, where I reside, half of the 1.5 million condos are more than 30 years old, and many of those are near the ocean, where buildings tend to structurally deteriorate faster than those farther inland.

There are many reasons why calamities occur on properties and structures where we play, live, and work. In this book, I won't go into each one because millions of things can go wrong on a property that will adversely affect the well-being of its inhabitants. I will, however, explore the three main issues that account for the majority of the problems that can happen in a building. But at the end of the day, this is a Florida problem that, at its root, also has to do with money and the courage to reform a broken system whose influential actors usually know that lives continue to be in danger.

The reason I wrote this book

One of the reasons I decided to write this book is to alert the public to the fact that what led to Champlain Towers' collapse is a microcosm of what is occurring in our older buildings, and is a sample of what is in store for us in the future should we continue to neglect to modify our rules, laws, and behaviors. The confluence of issues at this building is a perfect example of the convergence of problems typically present in other older buildings, particularly in Florida. As such, this tragedy provides an ideal opportunity to explore the roots of the issues.

I was on CNN's Prime Time with Chris Cuomo's show a few days after the collapse and told him and his viewers, "I'm glad that Congress recently passed an infrastructure bill that provides repairs to crumbling infrastructure. However, if there is no money for repairs, this tragedy is just a taste of things to come, whether it's bridges or buildings." A colleague called me shortly after it aired and told me that the bill did not pass, much to my dismay. Is our political body so dysfunctional that we cannot agree on something so basic and obvious? I was even more dismayed when a large bridge in Pennsylvania collapsed a few months later (in January, 2022), likely due to a lack of maintenance that many knew beforehand should have happened. It was coincidental and ironic that President Biden was due to speak on infrastructure spending in Pennsylvania just a few hours after the collapse.

Introducing the main culprit: a lack of maintenance

One of the most important concepts I want people to understand is that if you spend $1 on maintenance today, you'll save $2 down the road. If you have an investment, you have to protect it, whether you are a homeowner, property manager, building superintendent, board member, or even a government official. Non-engineers such as lawyers, teachers, doctors, and homemakers often serve on condominium boards. Essentially, these are people without a background or understanding in building construction and maintenance. These boards are entrusted with millions of dollars and instructed to spend it wisely. Yet, they don't receive any training or education on managing and allocating those funds.

Often, boards are as much a reason why buildings fail as governments are. Money is often the root of the issue. Condominium boards tend to kick the can down the road for urgently needed repairs (as in the case of Champlain Towers), and the US government is dysfunctional and lacks the spirit of cooperation to pass a comprehensive infrastructure bill.

The common culprits

Notwithstanding, there are many reasons why structures fail. Some of the ones I will explore in this book are engineering design, construction, apathy, and ignorance. This book will explore some of the most common ones in light of Champlain Towers' "perfect storm" of occurrences.

Chapter 2

When Champlain Towers Collapsed

n Washington, DC, at around 1:30 AM on Thursday, June 24, 2021, Mike Strattion received a phone call that would forever change his life. 1,000 miles away, his wife frantically called him from the balcony of their 4th floor apartment and tried to describe a "sinkhole" in the concrete pool deck below her unit. A handful of residents were evacuating, having been awoken by the sudden partial collapse of the pool deck, and it was only a matter of minutes before half of the 12-story building collapsed, taking Mrs. Stratton and 97 other lives to their death.

The building collapsed in a "pancake" manner that left very little room for a miracle to occur as 25 million pounds of concrete slabs collapsed, one on top of another, leaving a smoldering mound of rubble. Engineers and emergency rescue workers spent weeks sifting through the remains to find possible survivors as experts began to try and piece together the reasons why such a collapse would happen to a relatively new building in the 21st century.

My girlfriend woke me early that fateful morning to tell me that a residential high-rise had collapsed. I initially assumed that this building was located in a developing country and not in the United States. As she told me that this building was located in Surfside, Florida, I began to panic, noting that I have visited many condominium buildings along the South Florida coast. I had visited Champlain Towers in 2017 when my company was hired to provide them with some waterproofing details for their parking garage. After providing Champlain Towers with the plans back in 2017, I never received a call from contractors asking questions or owners requesting that I provide the typical inspections during construction. I never heard the words "Champlain Towers" again until the collapse on June 24, five years later.

Did they not perform the repairs according to the plans I gave them? Did they not even heed my recommendation to perform concrete repairs at all? What could have happened so that they failed to more expediently perform required repairs? What is the confluence of issues that led to such a rare occurrence?

My mind raced uncontrollably that morning as I foolishly dressed up to take the 45-minute drive to the site, hoping that somehow I would be of use. Upon arriving, I saw the mayhem. People were crying in the street and hugging each other. The police were trying to control the growing crowd as news outlets were jockeying for position for the best views. The only thing I could do at the site was make a selfie video narrating the scene and describing the gut feeling that our construction and engineering industry somehow let the trusting public down. In that moment, I knew that I had to do something more, having performed engineering and construction for concrete repair up and down the coast for many years. Even before the collapse, I knew that there was a profound problem in the way old buildings were inspected, maintained, managed, and repairs financed. This is not to mention the laws in place that would allow residents to forego urgent repairs, and possible design and construction flaws that may have contributed to this tragedy. For years, my voice had been drowned out by people not having the courage to make important repair decisions, by legislators not backing laws to require funding for repairs, and by many others.

On that morning of June 24, somewhere deep inside I knew that this calamity would be a turning point.

What happened at Champlain Towers?

The collapse of the 12-story beachfront condominium called Champlain Towers killed 98 people and injured 11. The cause of this incredibly rare tragedy is still under investigation, but it is not the first building failure to result in injury and death.

The first two stories of the building contained a parking garage. The building sat on the top of this garage. Half of the parking garage supported the residences and offices, and the other half was essentially a pool deck. That pool deck had planters so that it didn't look like a parking garage for the tenants who used it. It had lounge chairs, plants, and tables.

One of the culprits of what happened on the night of the collapse is *spalling*. A spall is a piece of concrete that becomes dislodged from the building because the reinforcing steel inside the concrete rusts and expands to the point where the concrete ruptures. Spalling originates when saltwater seeps into the concrete, damaging and rusting the reinforcing steel. Understand that concrete is inherently porous. If you take a microscope and look at concrete, you'll see that it has many holes, nooks, and crannies, much like a sponge. Saltwater in the air in humid, coastal climates enters the concrete and eventually reaches the reinforcing steel where the rust takes hold. Continuing the human body analogy, I like to refer to spalling as a "cancer" that continues to grow under the surface.

Theoretically, there are many reasons why any collapse of an existing structure can occur. However, from my vantage point of having worked in South Florida for over 30 years as a structural engineer and concrete contractor, I can state that this tragedy happened due to a confluence of things ultimately culminating in disaster. I believe that spalling was one of the initial sparks that set off a chain reaction, ending in the building's collapse. But there were many issues in the building before this initial spark occurred.

Let's go back to 2017 when the Champlain Towers condominium board reached out to my company to provide a waterproofing detail for the planters and their pool deck. The waterproofing detail would stop water from entering the garage from the planters on the exterior pool deck above. Unfortunately, we realized more significant problems were present than just the need to waterproof the planters. There were conspicuous signs of spalling.

After assessing the planters, we offered the plans to the board. We had seen and advised them of this spalling cancer in the building. The problem with spalling is that until you fix it, it will keep growing. As it grows, it continues to debilitate the structure. Essentially, the board wanted me to put a Band-aid on the spalling issue.

If someone has bone cancer, you can't treat it with a Band-aid. You have to open the person up, go to the source, and physically remove the cancer. Then you cover it up again. Rather than hire me to conduct a full inspection of the entire garage, they had only hired me to do a detail for waterproofing. We warned them anyway.

The problem circles back to the Champlain Towers Board, which was in charge of managing the money. A condominium board has a fiduciary duty to spend money to keep all the tenants, employees, visitors, and residents comfortable and safe. Yet, they often lack the knowledge needed to make those critical decisions when large sums of money are on the table. Generally, board members are not engineers or other real estate or construction professionals.

When boards are told they must spend millions of dollars to make a significant repair (like fixing the concrete in their parking garage), many tend to not listen to the experts and kick the can down the road despite being warned. They pick the Band-aid rather than open up the body to remove the cancer. The "quick-fix" (or no fix) is the cheaper, faster solution that ruffles the least amount of feathers. And it is my opinion that this is the way that many associations behave in Florida when confronted with large expenditures for repairs and maintenance. I'm not necessarily blaming the boards, but also the lax laws that are in place that allow the repairs to be postponed indefinitely and reserve accounts to be underfunded.

One of the issues at Champlain Towers was that all the key players knew they had a problem. It was an open secret. They reached out to me to put band-aids on the building's cancer, but when I was hired, I didn't know anything about the political and financial discussions occurring in the background.

After we gave them the waterproofing details, I never heard back from Champlain Towers again until the unfortunate event happened. In South Florida, it is not uncommon for condominium boards to not go through with the design you have engineered for them or to procrastinate. The reasons are varied, but most of the time, it has to do with money. I've been through this many times in my 30 years of experience working with condominiums. But, again, I don't put the entire blame on the board members themselves since they are often naive on the complexity and responsibility of the post, the hours demanded of the job, and the fact that many sacrifice their sanity and even friendships in the hopes of doing what in their mind is the "right thing." Where I have seen many boards at fault is that they often fail to expediently heed their experts' advice.

Imagine if you were to stand in front of all your condominium neighbors and tell them that they will have to pay $2,000 a month in additional maintenance fees for repairs, and there is nothing they can do about it. You have made yourself many enemies that automatically think that you are somehow making money off of it (all board members are volunteers), or you are not getting a good enough deal on the contract, or simply that the repairs are not needed or can be postponed. Some individual Champlain Towers residents were being hit with assessments of up to $300,000. This is something that I am very sensitive about, and as such, I tell my clients that I am always available to speak directly to all the residents and answer any questions. Sometimes it works, sometimes it doesn't. Either way, my recommendation would be that the Florida legislature pass a law that would *require* boards to maintain healthy reserves and thereby remove the boards' burden of having to act as the "bad guy."

Chapter 3

Historical Perspective

n the beginning, it was the age of the cavemen. Structures were created from whatever materials were at hand. The elders passed down construction knowledge from generation to generation. There were no official building codes in ancient times, such as we have in this modern era. Everyone knew that this rock could support another stone or a piece of wood. Through trial and error, the methods and technologies of construction and engineering slowly advanced through the ages.

The ancient Egyptians and the power of gravity

As civilization advanced, so did engineering abilities and technologies. One of the most outstanding examples is the impressive ancient Egyptians.

Though they lacked concrete as we know it today, they used large rocks of limestone and granite with mortar to create their famous pyramids. Thousands of enslaved people lugged around these massive rocks to form the awe-inducing structures that still stand today.

Working with rudimentary technology and led by ingenious men, they combined large rocks that were held together with little more than the power of gravity. Using the rules and codes available to the Egyptians at the time, you could never build a high-rise structure like the ones we see today. The technology wasn't there in the form of steel and reinforced concrete. In ancient times, other civilizations halfway around the world were masterful in fitting ten-ton stones perfectly together so that there were no gaps in between. They did such a meticulous job that you would be hard-pressed to find an opening large enough to insert a piece of paper.

But even as these seemingly indestructible icons stand today, they were not exempt from the trial-and-error factor that we experience with our modern-day structures. According to records, the Egyptians tried building the pyramids at different angles so that, through trial and error, they discovered the perfect angle. Only then could the pyramids withstand the test of time. It's been 4,500 years since then. The pyramids are now considered one of the world's seven wonders and receive nearly 15 million visitors every year.

The ancient Greeks and the arch

Following the Egyptians came another great civilization: the ancient Greeks. The Greeks surpassed the Egyptians by further innovating in building construction.

"Let's take these stones and put them on top of each other," they said. "But let's take things one step further by inventing the arch." Using different columns and placing a triangle on top of them creates an arch for people to walk through. Arches were used to provide open spaces where people could walk through as opposed to the wholly enclosed space of an Egyptian pyramid. But even the arch had its setbacks. With an arch, you can't have long distances between columns like the distances we have in today's modern buildings. And without these distances, one is limited to the type of stresses the arch can withstand, and therefore is limited to the number of stories one can build upward.

As you can see, as time went on and technologies advanced, the buildings got bigger, better, and more technically advanced. But all along the way, humankind has always pushed the boundaries of developing better, safer, and more robust ways to construct, and has also rebounded and learned from experiences and mistakes to maintain progress. So, although it is a shame that this tragedy occurred, we owe it to future generations and those who died at Champlain Towers and their friends and family to do what we can to minimize the chances of this occurring again.

Hyatt Regency walkway collapse

July 17, 1981, was the day of a very tragic engineering error that killed many people. The Hyatt Regency Hotel located in Kansas City was a five-story building with a large open lobby on the first floor. On the fourth floor, the hotel had constructed a suspended walkway. When standing on the pedestrian walkway, you could see the people in the lobby below. The walkway stretched from one end of the lobby to the other. It was suspended from the ceiling above rather than from below by columns like most bridges.

While designing the walkway, the hotel wanted to save money, so they asked the engineer if he could redesign the bridge in a more "efficient" manner. The engineer signed off on the request. Unfortunately, they didn't realize that by changing the structure's support, they were making it weaker.

On the hotel's opening day, they hosted a huge party. All sorts of people headed up to try the novelty, but the walkway couldn't handle the load. The bridge came crashing down, killing over 100 people and injuring 216.

During the investigation, they determined that the engineer was at fault. They should never have agreed to let the hotel change the design and make it weaker. A state jury found that the engineer was guilty of "gross negligence" for the wrong design decision. The engineer eventually claimed full responsibility.

Engineers are in a unique position in terms of responsibility for their work. Many engineers like to say that doctors have a license to kill, but when an engineer builds something, the engineer is personally liable for a design flaw if someone gets injured or dies from a design flaw.

The engineer can go to jail or get sued. In most states, engineers wield much power. People defer to engineers to decide whether something is safe or not. As a result, engineers carry a great deal of responsibility. They are held to very high ethical and professional standards as far as the law is concerned.

Florida International University pedestrian bridge collapse

In 2018, Florida International University decided to build a pedestrian bridge over 8th Street ("Calle Ocho" as we locals endearingly refer to it), one of the main east-to-west streets in Dade County. The politicians agreed to the project but supported the idea that construction could not adversely affect traffic because it would cause too much disruption to the public.

The contractor agreed to the stated conditions and decided to rope off the site for one day and use giant cranes to install the prefabricated bridge. The bridge would be built and then placed above the street while traffic continued as usual. On March 15, 2018, they began the installation. Unfortunately, the structure failed under stresses during the bridge installation. As a result, the bridge came crashing down on eight vehicles waiting for the stoplight to turn green. Six people died and ten were injured in the tragedy.

As I will mention later in this book, there are many layers of responsibility and oversight in a project of this magnitude. You have engineers, subcontractors, suppliers, inspectors, contractors, the city inspectors, and special inspectors. Many of these layers overlap in responsibilities. You can visualize it as a chain that is only as strong as its weakest link. So who was negligent? Was it the "weakest link" or a combination of links? We need to get into some engineering basics to correctly answer this important question.

CHAPTER 4

Structural Engineering Basics

Structural engineering is typically at the center of any building collapse. As such, it is essential to understand some fundamental structural engineering concepts with regard to reinforced concrete. To understand the importance of reinforcing steel inside the concrete, I would first introduce the reader to some structural engineering basics and explain it with a rather oversimplified and unconventional analogy. There's often a rectangular piece of concrete in front of each parking spot in your typical public parking lot. It's called a "wheel-stop." Let's suppose for a second that there was no reinforcing steel inside this imaginary wheel-stop.

Now, imagine King Kong grabbing each end of the wheel-stop as he tries to pull it apart. He could easily tear it apart because the concrete does not withstand what we engineers call "tensile forces" very well. Now let's say that instead of pulling it apart, King Kong tries to compress it by bringing his two hands together from each end. That's an entirely different story. King Kong will have difficulty crushing the wheel-stop since concrete is very good at withstanding "compressive forces."

Understand that if we were to give this same King Kong a solid steel pole, and he grabs it by both ends and tries to pull it apart, King Kong will have a difficult time pulling it apart. Thus, concrete by itself (with no reinforcing steel) does not withstand high tensile forces, while steel does. So it was only a matter of time until someone asked themselves, "Why don't we put a piece of steel inside that concrete?" This way, it can withstand both tensile and compressive forces! Just over 100 years ago, this discovery began the modern reinforced concrete movement in construction. A wheel-stop that is made of concrete with reinforcing steel inside of it is able to withstand all sorts of forces it is subjected to, and therefore engineers and architects are able to build bigger and better structures.

Another basic engineering concept that is important to understand is that engineers typically design different concrete strengths for various uses. Concrete strengths in the US are measured by pounds per square inch, or "psi." The higher the psi, the stronger the concrete. Footings can have a design psi of around 3,500psi, as opposed to other critical structural elements such as beams and columns. Psi is a measurement of the compressive strength of concrete, but when reinforcing steel is added to the concrete, the concrete's structural properties increase significantly.

Please note that this book was written for the non-engineering types, as I oversimplify some complex engineering concepts. But at the end of the day, every building technology developed has its pros and cons regardless of the era in which it was discovered. I'm sure that the current, cutting-edge 3D-printed structures have their own set of disadvantages that, God forbid, may one day endanger the lives of their inhabitants.

The vast majority of high-rise buildings along Florida's coast are made with reinforced concrete which is, from a historical perspective, a relatively new building technology developed just over 100 years ago. Today it is considered the norm, though engineering and construction practices are constantly shifting to meet advancements in technology. I believe that if the Romans had learned to put reinforced steel inside their concrete the way we do now, the Parthenon would no longer exist. After a few hundred years, the steel would have wholly rusted away and left the structure to fail catastrophically. In the case of the ancient Romans, it is good for us that they only had stone, marble, and gravity to use.

Modern technology

How do we ensure that we create durable buildings when steel inevitably corrodes? Scientists and engineers are constantly devising ways to improve the current technology. Today, people are developing new technologies to maximize that sustainability. For example, instead of placing steel inside the concrete, someone has figured out a way to insert non-corroding fiberglass as reinforcement. Another innovation is to put microscopic fibers inside the concrete to give it additional strength. Others are experimenting with a graphene additive to provide concrete with enhanced properties that regular concrete does not have.

Everybody in the industry wants to outperform everybody else with the latest building engineering and construction technology. Another example is 3D printers. Desktop units spew out microscopic amounts of plastic that get stuck to one another until they create small items like key chains and other plastic parts. Multiply the size of that 3D printer by 100 and include a four-inch moving hose that spews out concrete. Today, contractors are making houses that way. I didn't believe it until I saw an entirely 3D-printed house for myself on YouTube. The bottom line is that there is a constant evolution where humankind's entrepreneurial spirit and creativity push the boundaries to build bigger, better, and cheaper, which has brought us to the here and now, where concrete and reinforcing steel are the building blocks of the modern city skyline worldwide.

CHAPTER 5

Negligence! The Ambulance Analogy

P eople say that a chain is only as strong as its weakest link. It takes one weak link in a solid chain for a total failure in a process. At times it may seem straightforward to see an accident and immediately blame that one weak link when, in fact, there may be many links that contributed in one degree or another to a mishap. To understand this concept, I have invented the "Ambulance Analogy."

There is a man called George driving down a dark road in the dead of night without his driving glasses. Normally, his wife puts the glasses in his bag when he makes long trips but this time she didn't. Suddenly, he sees a man dressed in black crossing the street and in his attempts to avoid the impact, he veers out of control and crashes into a non-lit pole recently installed by the local power company. Four hours later, an ambulance arrives on the scene and they lift George into the ambulance. Unfortunately, the ambulance driver drives off a cliff when his brakes fail, killing everyone in the ambulance, including George.

Who was negligent in George's death? Was it the person who crossed the road at night dressed in black? Was it the wife who forgot to give George his glasses? Was it the power company that failed to install a light pole correctly? Was it the emergency medical worker who didn't check the brakes before he got into the ambulance or the mechanic who had maintained the vehicle a few months earlier? Was it the hospital's fault for not having enough ambulances, causing a four-hour delay in its arrival? The questions can go on forever.

I am not a lawyer, nor do I profess to be one. This "ambulance analogy" is not intended as a legal quandary to be studied and figured out. This is just a philosophical exercise so that the reader can understand that if you are looking to assign blame for negligence, you are in for some highly complex thinking.

The fact is that a particular confluence of events occurred. Some of these events could even be described as innocuous. The planets aligned in a way that led to George's death. We'll never know exactly where to place the blame in that situation, and if everyone in this story decided to lawyer up, this case could go on for years because all the arguments will have their own merits.

A chain of events is also responsible for the Chaplain Towers condominium collapse in Surfside, Florida. Around midnight, a woman on the second floor woke up to a loud bang. While standing on her balcony, she called her husband to tell him there was a gaping hole on the pool deck. That hole was the part of the pool deck that had collapsed. The pool deck was gone, and in its place was the large hole or, as she would describe it in her last words, a "sinkhole." What happened next was a tragic domino effect triggered by the initial failure of one of the structural components in the building.

When one element failed, the other elements failed after it. It's similar to what happened to poor George. You have the Champlain Towers condominium board that delayed the urgent repairs. You have the roofers who installed additional roofing materials on top of the original roof, adding weight to the building. You have the engineers and the contractors. There is much "blame" to go around. The real question is, what percentage of responsibility does each person or group bear? The answer is something the attorneys must hash out in a process that may take a long time to complete.

After watching what happened in Surfside, I felt an overwhelming sense of failure. That failure is not on my part individually but rather on the part of all who are involved in the construction and engineering industry, including politicians, insurance workers, managers, and so on. As an experienced licensed engineer and contractor, I know many people in the industry, and I don't know of one licensed engineer or contractor who would want to do something that could injure people. As of May 12, 2022, the parties in the Champlain Towers case had agreed to an almost $1 billion settlement, just shy of the one year anniversary of the collapse.

CHAPTER 6

Negligent Engineering? What Could Have Gone Wrong?

T he very day that the Champlain Towers collapse occurred on June 24, 2021, was the same day that the CIAPR's annual convention began in Orlando, Florida. The CIAPR is a Puerto Rican professional engineers' association with more than 10,000 licensed engineers as members; I was a board member of the organization's US mainland chapter in the past. I was also the main sponsor of the event and as such, I was obliged to attend. But before I left for Orlando, I was able to get my hands on the original structural engineering plans of Champlain Towers from 1980.

So imagine this: I was familiar with the building, I had the structural plans, and I was at a professional engineers' convention with many other professional engineers. Everyone had their theories on the root cause of the problem. After reviewing the original blueprints, we developed a few theories as to what may have caused this tragedy and determined, to the best of our abilities, why the condominium collapsed the way that it did.

You see, structural engineers are the professionals that structurally design the building so that it will comply with code and is thus safe for people to occupy it. Structural engineers must surpass arduous educational, training, and licensing requirements, and it takes a team of experienced engineers to design a multi-story structure such as Champlain Towers. Contractors construct buildings according to the exacting requirements of the plans made by these structural engineers. These plans indicate the precise sizing of each beam, column, and slab, their spacing from each other, and the exact size, quantity, and spacing of the reinforcing steel that goes into each of these structural elements, which comprise the building's "skeleton."

There were many pages to the Champlain Towers set of plans, and my engineering colleagues and I spent some time during this convention reviewing these plans to see if we could find any reason why this building could collapse as it did. We all agreed on several items.

First off, it was way too early to come up with solid or even probable theories when there were too many "moving parts" to this puzzle. The other pieces to this puzzle included possible original construction defects, the severe spalling in the garage, the fact that there was previously documented settlement in the garage, and that a roofing contractor had loaded the roof with his roofing materials just before the collapse. Our collective heads spun as we drew other theories, from the probable to the far-fetched.

We saw videos and pictures of the rubble. The images in the aftermath revealed that columns were jutting out of the ruins, which pointed to a "punching shear" problem. This punching shear was either the straw that broke the camel's back or, at a minimum, a contributing factor to the collapse. What is punching shear? Without going into any significant structural engineering theory, let me explain by having you perform a simple exercise. Put your left hand about six inches in front of your forehead with your palm faced down towards your feet. Now use the index finger of your right hand to press upward against your left hand in the exact place where your ring finger and middle finger meet. If you press your index finger upward with enough strength, your index finger will penetrate between the fingers of your left hand. In other words, your index finger "punched through" your left hand, and the weak point was where your middle finger and your ring finger meet.

In the Champlain Towers collapse, it seemed as though the structural connection from the column (your index finger) and the slab (your left hand) was weak. Was it weak because of the spalling concrete? Was it weak because the engineers designed it this way? Was it weak because the contractor did not go by the plans and built that connection incorrectly? The weakness may be attributable to one or all the above. This punching shear was a definite red flag, but is a tiny piece of a very complex puzzle to be resolved if we are to understand why this collapse occurred.

NIST's (National Institute for Standards and Technology) investigation is ongoing. It could take years to determine who or what should take the blame—whether it falls on the engineers who didn't design the structure correctly, the contractors who didn't construct correctly, or a combination of other unsuspecting players and circumstances. So what is the "measuring stick" that lawyers will use to determine the negligence, if any? They will likely start by investigating the proper adherence of the plans to the building code that was current when Champlain Towers was designed and built.

What are building codes?

Building codes are the rules that contractors, engineers, and architects have to follow when designing and building a structure. Different codes are observed in different areas. For example, the US codes are different from the ones used in China. Even in the US, the codes used in Florida, where buildings are designed for hurricane wind forces, are different from those used in California, where buildings are designed to withstand earthquakes.

Building codes are living documents that change over time to keep up with the latest technologies, materials, design, and construction methods. At times, codes are upgraded because of a mishap, as occurred in Miami upon the passing of Hurricane Andrew in 1992, and that is likely to occur because of the Champlain Towers collapse.

Today, we use some technologies that didn't exist 10, 20, or 30 years ago. The codes, in turn, must keep up with those new technologies. Typically, there is a board or a committee composed of different professionals. They could be engineers, architects, or politicians. Those boards have the responsibility to decide when and how to upgrade the code.

In Florida, the code changes every three years. During those years, the boards and committees meet to analyze what new technologies are prominent. For example, they might discuss what happened at Champlain Towers in Surfside, the emergence of new technologies, or discuss requirements to make structures more energy-efficient.

"Wait, there's a weak link here that we need to look into," they may say. "We need to change the code so that these things don't happen again. Maybe we need to increase the oversight by the building department or the engineers." It's the committee's responsibility to strengthen the code and make it better over time.

So, the question remains: what fault did the original structural engineers have in the collapse of Champlain Towers? The truth is that we currently do not know, and we may never know precisely to what extent they were negligent. Today, structural engineers can "backward design" Champlain Towers according to the old code and compare their findings to how Champlain Towers was initially designed. We can then determine, with a reasonable amount of certainty, if the original structural engineers designed the building correctly.

William Friedman, Architect

It is worth noting that the original architect, William Friedman, had a less than stellar career prior to becoming the principal designer for Champlain Towers. Years earlier, Friedman had designed some commercial sign pylons at the top of a building in downtown Miami, and in 1966 the Board of Architecture temporarily suspended Friedman, stating that he "negligently, improperly, and carelessly" designed that structure. Let me be clear that I am not blaming Mr. Friedman for the Champlain Towers collapse, but rather aim to spotlight the fact that human error has often been a factor in structural mishaps and tragedies.

It didn't help the designer's case when it was discovered, through some good investigative work by the Miami Herald, that the supporting columns at the lower levels of Champlain Towers were too narrow and thus did not meet the code requirements, and certain connections were not as strong as they could have been. These are preliminary findings, and the NIST is conducting a more detailed investigation. I am looking forward to reading their conclusions.

Haiti

On the other end of the spectrum with regard to building codes, we have countries such as Haiti, where there is little oversight in modern engineering and construction methodologies. I visited Haiti many times in the aftermath of the 2010 earthquake. In my quest to perform structural investigations, I interviewed many people. One of the more surprising things I discovered is that

Haiti has no nationally-recognized building code. Haitian engineers use a mix of American, European, and Canadian regulations on scant occasions. The death toll in this earthquake was up to 200,000, and the main culprit was inadequate design and construction methods.

Licensed professionals are your first line of defense against a dangerous structure. In a later chapter, I will explain the multiple overlapping layers of review and oversight that a building must withstand for it to be designed and built—from the developer's initial idea to the Building Department's approval and final issuance of the Certificate of Occupancy. The existence of these layers will be true in most of the developed world and is one of the main reasons why a collapse of this nature is extremely rare.

CHAPTER 7

Negligent Construction? What Could Have Gone Wrong?

The wild, wild west

After the Champlain Towers collapse, I received many phone calls. One of the most important came from a mentor and old friend who had been in Florida's engineering and construction business for over 50 years. The company he worked for built billions of dollars worth of construction throughout the US and the Caribbean. Very few people have his breadth of experience.

"Greg, I will tell you something," he said. "There's a perspective you don't know." He proceeded to share some very relevant information on the history of construction in Florida. There was a boom in condo construction in the 1980s fueled partially by the disastrous deregulation of the savings and loans associations, a surge of Latin American investors, and drug money. Champlain Towers South—the specific building that collapsed—was completed in 1981.

My mentor was a younger guy back then, and he found himself in the mix of building condos in South Florida during that time. "Greg," he told me gravely, "back then, it was no man's land. It was the wild, wild west out here." After further investigation and speaking to other contractors during that time, I realized that it was indeed the wild west where cutting corners was the order of the day, and bribing inspectors was not uncommon.

Many contractors at the time did not place a high priority on listening to engineers or what their plans and designs directed them to do. For example, if the plans stated a building needed five pieces of steel inside a column, they would put three pieces instead to save money and maintain a rapid pace. The problem was that there was not as much oversight and accountability as there is today. No building department reviews existed as they do today to review such work. There were also many stories of people being paid under the table.

Throughout the late seventies and early eighties, new condominiums were cropping up all along the coast in South Florida. Concrete manufacturers were challenged to keep up with the demand. One of the solutions was to build concrete batching plants right on the beach. There, they would batch their own concrete, at times using saltwater in the mix. Batching is a process where large silos are used to mix different ingredients together. After mixing these ingredients, the contractors poured the concrete into forms that ultimately created the beams and columns for the building structures. The biggest issue was that the steel corrosion is built into your structure when you start with saltwater inside the concrete mix.

Many buildings on the coast suffer substantial damage from reinforcing steel that has deteriorated within the structure over time, and as a contractor who began my career in 1991, I always heard rumors of people doing crazy things like using ocean water in the concrete mix. I would never have believed it, though, had it not come from my sources who had been first-hand witnesses, and when the fall of Champlain Towers in Surfside happened, it started to make sense.

When Hurricane Andrew hit Miami

In 1992, a year into my construction career, Hurricane Andrew descended upon Miami and caused billions of dollars of damage, making national headlines. At the time, I was a field engineer and had just completed one of the high-rises on the famed Fisher Island in Miami. Following this event, apartment and condominium building regulations became much stricter. The hurricane helped uncover the fact that many building roofs had been incorrectly installed. For example, only one or two nails would be used to fasten down a truss when the building plans required five fasteners. It was no secret to anyone in the industry that cutting corners was widespread.

This mentality did not change until Hurricane Andrew's damage and destruction caused insurance companies to lose millions. After Andrew, they demanded greater accountability in the system. As a result, building departments, officials, and city inspectors were required to perform more rigorous and detailed inspections to ensure code compliance.

After Andrew, Florida's building codes changed for the better. It went from the South Florida Building Code to the Florida Building Code, affecting all construction projects statewide. As a result, accountability was more fully integrated into the system. But what other risks of aging condos are lurking beneath the surface for these buildings that were constructed when the industry lacked more intensive oversight? I am afraid that we are only beginning to find the answer to that question.

CHAPTER 8

Negligent Residents and Owners? What Could Have Gone Wrong?

Florida Condo Act

I've saved what I consider to be the most important issue for last: negligence on the part of a community association, its board members, residents, and owners. I know it sounds harsh, but it's the truth in a broad sense. I've lived in Florida for many years and have owned multiple properties with community associations set up like the one Champlain Towers had. These community associations are created, managed, and operated under Chapter 718 of the Florida Statute, known as the "Florida Condominium Act." The law requires that these condominiums be managed by a board comprised of owners who have the fiduciary responsibility of making decisions for the benefit of all the other owners and residents. Many of these decisions have to do with budgets, of which repairs, maintenance, and capital improvements form a significant portion. When large expenses are required (such as making significant structural repairs), many boards face the unenviable decision to spend the money to get the work done, or simply kick the can down the road. Whenever I deal with a condominium client that needs a certain amount of structural work done, the immediate questions are, "how much will it cost?" and "where do we get the money?"

Boards are formed when other owners at the property vote them in through an election that typically happens every year. Being on a board is hard work carried out by volunteers who don't necessarily have the experience to run a company, manage a large budget, or are not educated in the real estate, engineering, construction, or property management industries. It is a complicated, time-consuming, and mostly thankless job. My heart goes out to the hundreds of board members I have encountered in my 30 years of business. The vast majority take on this significant responsibility because they legitimately care about the place where they live. Most sacrifice time with their families, loved ones, and even their careers to responsibly undertake this difficult post.

Having dealt with many boards that have faced this struggle, I can attest that many choose to procrastinate rather than face the wrath of those who think that the repairs are unnecessary and can be done later, or who don't trust the current board in charge. When reserves are not maintained and funds are low, boards revert to obtaining loans and special assessments, which can be a huge burden to those owners who cannot readily afford it.

As much as board members sincerely want to do the right thing by their fellow residents, they are human, and many make the mistake of not seriously heeding the calls of professionals. Instead, many board members put their heads in the sand, are indifferent, or do not want to risk straining their relationships with their neighbors.

Florida law gives condominium boards the power to raise money, but does little to require these boards to make necessary repairs that could, if performed promptly, avoid bodily injury or save lives. The reality is that these boards are allowed to neglect funding the reserves (the association's rainy-day piggy bank, if you will) that would be used to perform these repairs. If a requirement for funding these reserves is not present, it is pretty much left up to the board to make the difficult call of obligating the owners to pay up, or kicking the can down the road. Unfortunately, many choose to kick the can down the road. And currently, Florida law allows this procrastination to occur.

Residents and owners on the front line

Residents and owners are on the front line in making sure that their place of residence is safe. You don't have to be an engineer or construction professional to know when something is broken or when that crack you saw last year has become wider and longer. Likewise, you don't need an advanced degree to understand that a piece of concrete falling from the building is a huge red flag. Anyone can see water stains on walls and floors or notice when the power consistently flutters. The obvious tell-tale signs that something is wrong are almost infinite.

Several years ago, I performed an inspection of the crawlspace of an older building in Miami. I had received a phone call from a resident who noticed that part of the first floor was "spongy" as they walked across it. It is typical in Miami Beach for older structures to have their floor structures made out of wood which, in turn, would be supported by a concrete beam or foundation of some sort. I put my Tyvek suit on and entered the crawl space where no one had been in several years, and my heart sank as I saw a vast concrete beam supporting the center of the building with a crack large enough I that could fit a finger in it. The beam had structurally failed, and about 20% of it was reduced to concrete rubble on the dirt below. This was the reason that the wood floor felt "spongy." I immediately took my pictures and findings to the owners and told them that the building must be immediately evacuated unless this beam was properly shored that same day. The beam was shored that same day, and the repairs were promptly performed. I firmly believe that if the owners had not identified this beam and then immediately repaired it, the chances that this could have eventually become a tragedy are significant. Fortunately, it only took a phone call from a concerned resident who noticed something was wrong.

Please note that the same concept will apply whether you live in a condominium with a board, own a commercial building, or live in a single-family home located in the middle of nowhere. It literally takes one phone call.

Having dealt with hundreds of clients and condominium boards in South Florida, I can state that condominium boards bear much of the responsibility for the lack of maintenance of a building. But the fact is that the current laws in Florida allow boards to use the reserves in the budget for items other than structural repairs. It is my opinion that there should be a law that would require boards to save money in the reserves for the eventuality of a much-needed structural repair. In the absence of such a requirement, boards have the authority to defer these repairs indefinitely.

During the early years of my company, one client of mine was in dire need of structural repairs to their elevated concrete pool deck, which had significant signs of spalling and other structural issues. Instead of making the repairs, they decided to remodel the interior hallways of their oceanside 200-plus-unit building with plush carpeting, new LED lights, and a fresh coat of paint. As the engineer, I was alarmed and upset that despite my recommendation to have them perform the structural repairs, they nonetheless fired me and proceeded with the aesthetic upgrades with their new interior designer. Although I was upset, little did I realize that this story was to repeat itself over and over again with other clients in the future.

A few years ago, another large oceanside 200-plus-unit condo hired me to provide engineering plans and specifications for concrete repairs. When they received the bids for construction, they realized that the project would cost them about two million dollars. Several residents formed a committee that would ultimately use the Florida condominium law to revoke the existing board and stop the costly construction in its tracks. The basic reasoning was that they did not trust the current board and that the repairs were, in their minds, unnecessary. The hatred was so great that some residents obtained restraining orders against one another so they could not be within 50 feet of each other. I remember one tense meeting where one of the residents had to sit 50 feet away from one of the board members. Luckily, the meeting room was large enough that both residents could sit at the established minimum distance. To make a long story short, I was fired from the job by the new board because they wanted to have a fresh start with a clean set of eyes. Because there was so much distrust between residents, the new board hired another engineer to redo the engineering that I had already done (and thus they paid twice for it) and proceeded to perform the work anyway at the same cost that I had forecast.

Believe it or not, I have many similar stories.

The Haiti dilemma

Every place uses some sort of building code in one form or another, even if that building code is the information passed down from your forefathers. Often, developing countries lack the infrastructure and education systems to sustain an efficient and robust building code. Essentially, people will build houses as their friends, fathers, and grandfathers taught them.

I discovered this first-hand when I visited Haiti after their major earthquake in 2010 to help assess the damages. "What does the code say?" I asked everyone I encountered. "Who was managing the code and enforcing the rules?" The answer did not differ among the dozens of people I surveyed. "What are you talking about?" they asked incredulously. "There is no code. Nobody is enforcing anything." "Surprised" is a mild way to describe my reaction. Amidst all the death and destruction, the Haitians were ill-prepared for the massive damage caused by a 7.0 magnitude earthquake.

It was no wonder the country fared so poorly. The Haitians did not design and construct many buildings to withstand such monumental forces. For example, while driving around, we often saw people on the side of the road gathering concrete. I watched them take hammers to the concrete blocks and begin to pulverize them. Finally, I approached some of these people to ask what they were doing. As the man crushed a cinder block before my eyes, he explained that he would take the crushed pieces and mix them with water, producing a concrete-like substance afterward. Then he would sell the refurbished material to people who would eventually use it to construct other buildings.

That recycled concrete is the cheap, weak version of a product they would sell at a Home Depot to secure fence posts. However, there are no codes or regulations to sanction the creation and production of such a product. These Haitians would recycle their cement and sell it forward. The great majority of people there believe they are doing the right thing because it's the way they have been taught, or their circumstances have forced them into doing it. It's gone on this way for many years, and continues today.

I had never previously visited Haiti. During my trips, I was in awe of the people's resilience, ingenuity, resourcefulness, and good-heartedness. It is a shame that Haiti does not have the infrastructure to support a system that promotes sound engineering and construction practices. I'm sure that most Haitians will agree with me that this is a crucial issue to tackle.

CHAPTER 9

What Can You Do to Avert Disaster at Your Building?

First, don't panic

In the months after Champlain Towers collapsed, my office received hundreds of phone calls from people legitimately concerned about their buildings. Some people heard creaking sounds in their attic, others saw unusual cracks that they had not noticed before. Many were panicking. I do not blame these people for being extra conservative since structural problems can eventually cause injury and even death.

The main reason I wrote this book is to educate people and to help them understand the realities surrounding what it is to have a safe building, when to be concerned, and the steps to take to address concerns. Panic is usually borne out of a lack of knowledge. After receiving hundreds of phone calls, I tried at first to speak to each person to communicate that although they should have a concern, they should temper that concern with some education. In dealing with each caller, I noticed a pattern of questions and concerns. This eventually led to me creating a free live webinar called "Averting Disaster at your Building" less than one month after the collapse, and hundreds of people tuned in. Although you can now find a recording of this webinar on YouTube, this book is much more in-depth and detailed on the subject.

I don't want to be alarmist in stating that you should go out and immediately and have your building inspected by an engineer (that is, unless you see something that raises a red flag). I am also not saying that you should remain action-less. Instead, you should be alert to your surroundings and note things you may see that are "off."

When building a large structure or even a house, everyone hires a design professional such as an architect or an engineer to create the design. A design professional has the experience, education, and a license to design a safe and comfortable building for its occupants. They are also assuming responsibility for the safety and effectiveness of the structure. For this reason, the architect will hire a structural engineer for the more complex projects, who will determine how much steel should go into that column, what size the beams should be, and where they should be located.

Once you have your plans, the next step is to hire a contractor to carry out this plan. For this discussion, let's assume that your architect has hired a competent contractor like Turner Construction. They're highly skilled people who know enough to do an excellent job with the given information. You now have three layers of professionals looking at the same design: the architect, the engineer, and the contractor.

Before you get started on the actual building, you have to obtain a permit for the construction. To do so, you must give your plans to the local building department. The building department typically performs a professional review to ensure that the design is done correctly. In that review, engineers from the building department look at your plans and decide whether it all looks OK or suggest changes. That constitutes your fourth level of review.

Finally, when the construction begins, you will also have city building inspectors, including the contractor's inspectors, scrutinize the project as it is being completed.

You have the eyes of the owner, who is paying for the whole thing. You have the contractors, who are supervising their people. You have the engineers and the architects, who are responsible for the plans. And last but not least, you have the inspectors from the building department who many see as a pain, but in reality, they are there to help ensure that the laws and codes are followed. After all, these rules, codes, and laws fundamentally protect public safety.

Second, understand your building is like a human body

The guts of a building are a very complex web of concrete, steel, aluminum, glass, and piping. They are made up of various systems ranging from computer cabling and security wiring to fire sprinklers, sanitary systems, ductwork, garbage disposal, and water supply systems, among many others.

Like most people, you probably don't think twice about all these systems whenever you walk into a building. They work in harmony to offer you a safe environment with the right temperature and breathable air. People take that for granted and fail to realize the existence of an entire ecosystem running behind the scenes.

As an engineer, when I walk into a building, I look past the color of the walls, the lighting fixtures, or the lovely marble floors. These are small, surface-level parts of the complexity of the entire building. Instead, I see the complicated array of systems working to keep me safe and comfortable.

Because a building is like a human body, if one system fails, something else will fail too. Our skeletal structure represents the concrete. If our skeletons disappear, we will be reduced to a piece of mush and will proceed to collapse to the floor. If my shin bone, the tibia, breaks or disappears, my whole body will collapse. Even a tiny bone like your ankle bone affects your entire body.

The same goes for your digestive system or nervous system. Your nervous system is like a building's electrical system, while your digestive system is the plumbing. Your muscle is the drywall.

However, your skin is one of the most essential elements of your body. It is your first line of defense, ensuring that microbes and germs can't get into your body. Your skin repels them, and your white blood cells go into action. You're constantly being protected from germs every day just by your skin.

With a building, you need a good paint job because the paint is the skin of your structure. You also need a waterproofing system on your floors and a good watertight roof. Otherwise, any dirt or chlorides from the air will seep into the concrete. Many people don't realize how much the building's skin matters and thus don't maintain their buildings. Instead, they let the paint fade away, debilitating the building's skin and making it much more susceptible to damage. Hopefully, through viewing your building as a human body, you will take better care of it.

Third, understand that proper (and timely) maintenance is critical

In the same way that you have a doctor who provides you with a yearly checkup, an engineer can scour through your building and tell you what items need maintenance or repairs. In Florida, we have a 40-Year Recertification inspection requirement mandating that buildings must undergo a detailed inspection by a professional when the building turns 40 years old. Champlain Towers' 40-Year Recertification was performed prior to the collapse, and the engineer that performed the inspection called out the structural damage present and urged the board to take action. Unfortunately, the building collapsed as the project was starting. Other states may have some type of inspection requirement to command residents and owners to keep a finger on their building's pulse. For example, California's Health and Safety Code requires 15% of each type of structural element (i.e., balconies, walkways, and stair landings) to be tested every six years.

In my experience in Florida, most of the buildings that I have inspected have issues that should be addressed. Every once in a while, I come across a building where repairs are urgently needed. Fortunately, the system is set up so that residents and owners can hire the right people and get the work performed.

I often tell my clients that "a stitch in time saves nine." It's an adage that I repeat in letters, reports, and meetings with residents and owners. Many people do not realize how important proper maintenance of a building is. What if I were to ask you, "What would you rather pay: $50,000 now, or $200,000 in ten years?" It's ironic that although the vast majority of people reading this question would rather pay the $50,000 now, the fact is that many of my past clients have expressed, through inaction on the maintenance of their building, that they would rather pay the $200,000. I emphatically state that had Champlain Towers performed proper maintenance in their building and completed needed repairs as they appeared, there would still be 98 souls present with us today.

For example, one of my clients is an affluent, oceanside, high-rise condominium that is over 40 years old. Years ago, they hired me to provide a water intrusion assessment at one corner of the building. Twenty of their units had water leaks, damaging the drywall whenever it rained and causing mold. They explained that for several years this had been an ongoing problem. Before my inspection, they would repair leaks, add drywall, replace baseboards, and cover holes as they were discovered. I told them that they also needed some concrete repair. When they told me that the building had not been painted in 20 years, I proceeded to tell them that they should urgently perform repairs and paint the entire building, including re-caulking all the windows (which were the source of many leaks). I never received a call-back at that time.

Fast forward ten years after that initial inspection, and I received a phone call from that very same condominium. It turns out that they had neither painted nor repaired the concrete and opted to kick the can down the road. Hoping that they would finally have the courage and money to do the work, they approved my proposal to perform plans and specifications for the concrete repair and painting. To make a long story short, the updated price to complete the repairs was millions of dollars, a far cry from my initial estimate. Similarly, Champlain Towers' ultimate repair cost just before the collapse was fifteen million dollars. Had the residents made the repairs when the damages were first discovered, the price tag would have been significantly less. Spalling concrete is like cancer and grows at an accelerated rate each year that repairs are not made.

The importance of constantly providing maintenance does not only apply to the concrete and "skin" of the building, it also applies to equipment, elevators, windows, doors, finishes, plumbing systems, and air conditioning. The list goes on and on. However, for this book, I will review the three most essential items that comprise 90% of the problems in buildings from a financial perspective. These are concrete and structural issues, building envelope issues, and electrical issues.

CHAPTER 10

3 Items That Comprise 90% of Building Problems

Item 1: concrete and other structural issues

The majority of the critical problems in a building, considering lives at stake, are structural. We depend on a sturdy structure to protect us from hurricanes, earthquakes, rain, and wind. However, many forget that Father Time also takes a toll on structures, whether made of wood, steel, or concrete.

Wood is an organic material susceptible to failure due to termite infestations and decomposition. Notwithstanding, our ancestors used wood for thousands of years, and it is still used today with great success. Today's technologies allow us to build large wooden structures with special steel fasteners and plates. Glulam beams, which consist of many pieces of wood glued together to form vast beams and columns, are effectively used by engineers and architects to design marvelous and beautiful structures. Modern technologies have also developed additives that are infused into wood to deter termites from invading, or to make the wood less susceptible to rot. Yet wood remains an organic material that will fail if not properly maintained. Proper wood maintenance includes painting, sealing, and periodically inspecting the main structural elements.

Steel is vulnerable to rusting, but it is also one of the cheapest, most durable, and versatile building materials. However, if not appropriately maintained, guarding its surface against water and oxygen, your structure will rapidly deteriorate. The Golden Gate Bridge is an excellent example of how a steel structure can survive a hostile oceanside environment, given that it is subjected to a rigorous maintenance schedule. The bridge's upkeep costs many millions of dollars per year and requires a workforce of around 200 people that includes ironworkers, painters, and electricians.

Concrete can fail, as occurred at Champlain Towers, due in part to severe spalling and corrosion of the reinforcing steel inside the concrete. Concrete is inherently porous, allowing saltwater particles to enter the concrete and cause the reinforcing steel (or "rebar") to rust. Once the rust begins, the steel expands, as anyone with a rusty car or lawn chair can attest to. A rusted piece of steel can expand up to seven times its original volume and can cause the concrete to rupture under that expansive pressure. If not repaired, the spalling will continue to weaken the structure and spread like cancer until the ultimate failure of the affected components.

Another common concrete structure ailment is settlement, where the dirt underneath the structure gives way and causes the structure to move and sink. These movements can cause cracks in the walls, beams, and columns of the structure. In some cases, the cracks eventually become a danger to those living in the structure. Let me start by stating that all structures move and settle to one degree or another. When one side of the structure moves more than the other, we get what we call "differential movement," and cracks appear. These cracks are a red flag that lets the engineers know that there may be a deeper issue at stake. Engineers study the crack's size, length, and location to determine the urgency at which it needs repair. Periodic inspections by an engineer, like those performed in Florida through the 40-year recertification process, are critical in identifying potentially dangerous structural problems.

There are many reasons structures fail due to a lack of vigilance and maintenance. It is beyond the scope of this book to discuss the many other structural problems that can arise in a building. Here, we focus on concrete spalling since it is the most prevalent structural issue for concrete structures, and it is at the center of the Champlain Towers collapse. For a more detailed explanation of concrete spalling and the process for repair, please refer to Appendix A.

Item 2: building envelope issues

What is the "building envelope"? Simply put, the building envelope separates the outside from the inside. It protects us from rain, wind, and adverse outside temperatures. In other words, it is the "skin" of the building comprising the windows, roof, doors, floor, walls, stucco, veneers, insulation, and siding (among many other components). Once the envelope is compromised, a domino effect eventually commences, ultimately rendering a structure uninhabitable.

For example, water and moisture intrusion is the most common and destructive source of a building envelope failure. Water can enter a habitable area through the smallest of cracks and openings. These openings appear on concrete, old windows, roofing, worn and brittle caulking, and other origins. Moisture causes tiles to dislodge, invites insect infestations, causes concrete to spall, among many other issues. Additionally, moisture damages most interior finishes including paint, drywall, baseboards, and cabinetry. On the more serious side, moisture causes mold, adversely affecting the health of inhabitants.

A good paint job is the number one defense against building envelope issues. Many people think that painting is just a can of paint, a brush, and a person to apply it to a wall. However, painting is very complex if it is to be correctly executed. Professional painters are adept at identifying and sealing cracks on the walls and pinpointing failures in the caulking around windows and doors. Good painters take as much care in preparing the substrate to be painted as applying the paint itself. This means sealing holes and cracks, repairing caulking, performing minor stucco and concrete repairs, and even testing certain areas to ensure that their work is satisfactory.

Water can enter a property and damage the insulation, another critical component of the building envelope that helps regulate the temperatures inside the structure. Insulation keeps the heat inside during the winter and the cold inside during the summer when your air conditioning is running.

Caulking also needs regular maintenance. It's very pliable when you first install it, but over time it becomes brittle and susceptible to cracking. Low-grade caulking may last a year, while high-grade caulking can last up to 20 years. However, no matter how high-quality the caulking, the caulking can quickly fail if the building hasn't been maintained or painted in many years. If you use a knife to scratch out some of old the caulking between the windows, you can see that it cracks like dry bubble gum. Those cracks are another place for the water to penetrate the building envelope.

Waterproofing treatment is also widely used to keep water out of a building. Think of waterproofing as a high-grade, expensive paint that is used in specific areas where water tends to accumulate. Waterproofing is installed on the back of retaining walls, on elevated walkways, inside exterior planters above a parking deck, and on decks where no one wants water seeping in. There are many companies that sell waterproofing materials, and each have their special applications, details, and methods of installation. Some waterproofing materials are expensive and tend to have warranties that last 20 or more years. Other waterproofing materials are cheap and do not last long. There are thousands of products available in the market that have different properties to be used in specific applications. It is beyond the scope of this book to discuss these in detail.

Performing painting, waterproofing, caulking, roofing, and other activities designed to keep water out of a building is an extremely complex range of fields. Specialty contractors such as painters, waterproofers, and roofers are experts in their particular fields and can provide you with information on how to best repair your water intrusion issues and methods to best maintain your existing systems. Hiring an engineer, however, is your best option to get an unbiased opinion on how best to deal with your current envelope. The key is to hire them (and listen to them) when the problem rears its head, and not years afterward. In 2017, Champlain Towers hired me to provide them with a waterproofing detail for the planter structures above the garage. Water was leaking from the planters, landing on the cars below, and ultimately damaging their structure. Simply put, it was a Band-aid repair to a larger problem they knew they had. It was too little, too late.

Item 3: electrical issues

I tell many of my 40-year recertification clients that no one has ever died from a leaking pipe, a lousy paint job, or a failed roofing system. However, many people have been killed in structural failures and electrical mishaps. In 1882, Thomas Edison formed the Electric Illuminating Company of New York to help bring electric power to parts of Manhattan. By 1925, half of the homes in the US had electrical power.

Although electricity significantly contributed to the nation's wealth, it also came with disadvantages. Electricity was hazardous if not handled properly and safely. By 1897, the NEC (National Electrical Code) was established to help manage design and construction standards. We have come a long way from those early days, but electricity remains dangerous and has been named as the culprit of many deaths by fire and electrocution.

The dangers that electricity poses are broad and complex. A whole set of books can be written about electrical design, construction, and safety. The NEC alone is almost 1,000 pages. Although it is beyond this book's scope to delve into electricity, it should suffice to say that a building's electrical system is like your body's nervous system. The nervous system allows your muscles to move, your eyes to see, your skin to feel, and powers your brain. In that same manner, you should treat your electrical system with respect and ensure it is properly maintained.

Some may ask, "How do you maintain an electrical system? It has no moving parts." Electrical systems must be maintained for the prolonged health of your building. I'll give you a few examples of how the electrical components of your building should be maintained:

Replace old, unsafe wiring. From the 1880s to the 1940s, many homes had a "knob and tube" system with attic wiring strung around porcelain knobs. These systems are no longer allowed. I have personally inspected older homes in Miami, found these systems, and advised the owners to replace them. The sheaths that surround the wires are often made of cloth which deteriorates, rendering the system dangerous since the bare wires become exposed.

Inspect for wiring mistakes. Electricians are human and make mistakes. Do-it-yourselfers are also human. A contractor can make almost an infinite number of errors when dealing with electricity. Sometimes, the wrong wire sizes or breakers are used, or the grounding is incorrect. Most of these construction mistakes often do not rear their heads until it is too late and a fire starts. For example, if an electrician keeps a small wire inside a conduit and replaces the breaker from a 20-amp breaker to a 100-amp breaker, the wire will overheat and could cause a fire down the road .

As you can see, electrical issues are wide-ranging. If the electrical system is not maintained correctly, it could lead to malfunctioning equipment such as air conditioning or a more critical piece of equipment such as an elevator or fire alarm system. It is beyond the scope of this book to go into any significant detail on how to avert electrical accidents and mishaps. I do, however, want to reiterate that a good electrical maintenance inspection can help detect problems in your system that you may want to fix.

CHAPTER 11

Regular Safeguards

Wherever your building is located, the city requires various inspections. At minimum, the fire alarms are inspected every so often, along with the electrical systems. If you look in your elevators, you'll see a placard that says what date they were last inspected. All elevators across the country are required to be checked periodically.

An engineer or architect could be hired to certify that the building has these things running safely. Here in South Florida, there is a 40-year certification requirement. It's a law stipulating that a building must be inspected when it turns 40. Every city and state has its own set of rules, or lack thereof.

Throughout the world, countries and states have different rules and regulations. Canada has requirements to inspect buildings every ten or 20 years. Building departments understand that these inspections are necessary because, as I previously mentioned, facilities are like human bodies that need regular care. Canada also requires building associations to accumulate funds in advance for any potential projects.

Although some states in the US require inspections, it is not the same across the board. For example, certain areas of Florida have different regulations. Laws differ from Miami to Orlando to South Florida. Additionally, Florida doesn't require any funds to be set aside to pay for maintenance items like they do in Canada. On the other extreme, you have Haiti, with almost no building codes or inspection requirements.

How do we pay for it?

There are many different building loans available for repair and maintenance projects. Plus, interest rates today are relatively low. Financially, there is no excuse not to spring for at least a paint job. Otherwise, you're shooting yourself in the foot.

As a real estate investor, you always look out for your investment. People say, "The less I spend on that house or investment, the better." They think they're saving money and that it's going straight into their pockets. Beware of that mentality, though, because it's not necessarily true. It may very well be the opposite.

If you are not painting and maintaining your building, the issues will only worsen. Whether it's water intrusion or termites, you will see the money you thought would line your pockets instead going toward one of these dilemmas. What costs you $5 today will cost $50 next year. People look at maintenance as an expenditure, but it's an investment in your property.

Calling in the professionals

You may be worried or concerned about something in your building. You don't know what to do about it. Have no fear; there are a lot of professionals out there who have the expertise to help you out. The fact is that you don't have to be an engineer to point out a crack or some other anomaly that just doesn't look right. Although most cracks are not severe or life-threatening, you still shouldn't ignore a crack when you see it.

You wouldn't ignore a mole or a lump on your chest. It could be cancer, or it could be something innocuous.

Either way, you take that visit to the doctor as an investment in your health. You know your body better than anyone else, just like you know your apartment better and will notice if and when something is off.

On the same token, it's also essential to hire the right professionals. Different professionals are involved in repairing, constructing, or maintaining a building. If you find something wrong in your building and you're not quite sure what the problem is, or who to call, the general line of defense is a typical home inspector. These inspectors are licensed individuals with the education and experience in a broad range of construction and engineering issues. At a bare minimum, these inspectors will let you know if there is a specialist that you need to call if something is out of their area of expertise. A typical home inspection will cost around $400, depending on where you live, but it is better to call a person with sound fundamental knowledge than guess and go directly with a specialist. This is more or less the same as going to an expensive cardiologist when you have chest pain rather than visiting your generalist first, who may diagnose you with gas.

CHAPTER 12

When Buying, Watch Out For . . .

A t times you do not even live in a building and you would like to find out what state the property is in. For example, let's say you want to buy a nice condo by the beach. How do you know if the condo has any money in the bank to make future repairs? What if significant issues need to be addressed, and there is a possibility of a substantial assessment looming? The bottom line is that if you are going to make what is possibly one of the most significant investments of your life, then you should protect yourself by doing the following:

1. Hire an attorney to help you understand your situation and review the condominium documents if neces-

sary. These contracts at times hide certain things that you should know about up front.

2. You should ask the condominium board or the property manager for copies of the last 12 monthly meeting minutes. These will give you a pretty good picture of the main issues at the condo. You can ask for them, but there is no guarantee that you will get them. Different states have different privacy laws and rules for providing these documents.

3. You should ask the condominium board or the property manager for copies of financial statements, including the latest reserve study, which lets you know how much money is in the condominium's piggy bank to cover large expenses such as a new roof, a paint job, or replacing the elevators. Again, each state has its own rules about making these documents public. You should consult with an attorney to lead the way.

Why you should care about the reserve

The association's reserve, or condo reserve study, estimates the costs to repair and replace major common area components, such as roofs or pavement, over the long term. The reserve study projects a financial roadmap for the association as they move into the future.

I'll try to explain something complex with a simplistic example. Imagine you live in a building of 100 apartments. One of the housing association's board members informs you that the elevators need to be replaced. This is a considerable expense. Remember that your reserves are the amount of money you have in the bank for a rainy day, and if the reserve fund is zero, the owners must immediately shell out that money from their pockets.

If your monthly association fees are $100, with 100 units in the condominium, your monthly budget to make everything run smoothly is $10,000. That $10,000 is already budgeted for the building's typical costs, such as landscaping, utilities, and property management fees.

Let's say that it'll cost $50,000 to replace the elevators. Now you, as the tenant, are responsible for paying a share of that amount, in addition to the $100 you're already paying per month.

The $50,000 expense will now be spread out among the 100 owners as a special assessment (or $500 per owner). Instead of $100 per month, your dues will now be $200 per month for the next five months.

But suppose in the latest reserve study, the association opted to set aside $25,000 for elevator repairs, knowing that they would soon need some work. That would have reduced the need for a special assessment by half, and it would be much more manageable by all owners.

This is just a very small and simple example. The folks at Champlain Towers were looking at assessments between $80,000 per unit for the smaller apartments and up to $300,000 for the larger units for the needed concrete repairs. The total repairs were estimated at $15,000,000. Had Champlain Towers taken their maintenance more seriously and kept enough reserves in the bank, chances are that this tragedy would not have occurred. Furthermore, if the repairs had been performed years earlier, the repairs would have cost a fraction of the final price tag.

In Canada, they require an engineer to visit every condo to conduct a reserve study to help determine if additional money must be added to the tenants' monthly dues to cover potential repairs.

I have often been the bearer of bad news when a condominium has to incur millions of dollars of repair expense. The owners and residents do not always live in elegant ocean-side condominiums, but often in middle/lower-class condos farther inland. The challenges of obtaining the money are real, whether through assessments or bank loans. At times, condos cannot quickly obtain loans and are stuck with requiring the owners to pay directly out of their pockets. If these owners cannot pay, eventually, they are foreclosed on. I became an engineer to help people with their problems. It pains me to have people pay with money they don't have for repairs that they don't fully understand. But beyond everything, I am an engineer bound by oath to guard public safety, and every other engineer I know would do the same as me.

So why is it so prevalent in Florida that condominiums don't have enough money at times to perform large repair projects? In Florida, it is not a requirement to pre-emptively obligate residents to pay into their reserves, as it is in other states and countries. Therefore, there is often not enough money in the reserve fund account to pay for larger-scale projects when they arise. It is not uncommon for condominiums in Florida to have $0 in their reserves. As a final note, I'd like to mention that a reserve study is not an engineered inspection nor should it be construed as one. Reserve studies don't prevent collapses, but are merely a vehicle to estimate future maintenance expenses.

Is there money in the reserve?

Before the Surfside tragedy, Florida legislators tried passing a law that would require homeowner's associations to keep enough money in their reserves. Unfortunately, it did not pass. Now people are starting to have that conversation again. We will see if our lawmakers can make this happen.

The reserve must contain the funds necessary to cover potential projects like a new paint job or roofing. If Champlain Towers had had a fair amount of resources to cover the tasks that needed completion, the subsequent tragedy might not have happened.

Tenants protect themselves during the buying process by hiring a home inspector. Before purchasing any property, you hire a home inspector and get a report on the general health of the property. However, home inspectors are not responsible for investigating the homeowner's association reserve or assessing its financial health.

One critical action would be not only to hire a home inspector but also to ask your Realtor to go directly to the board and ask for a reserve study. Ask to see the meeting notes. For example, if the reserve study notes say zero dollars are in the bank, your first question should be, "Am I getting hit with a $50,000 assessment one day?"

People should have as much information as possible when making an important decision. It's similar to checking the nutrition facts on the back of your food at the grocery store. That gives you a good idea of whether something will be good for you or not before you ingest it. You want all the knowledge possible when deciding whether to make such a significant investment. For most people, buying a house or property is one of the most important decisions they will make over their entire lives.

There should be robust legislation that allows people to make these informed decisions. Prospective buyers should have access to any inspections to be made, building re-certifications, elevator evaluations, and reviews by other authorities attesting to the health or non-health of the property.

On the opposite side of that are the developers or landlords. They typically don't want prospective buyers to know everything there is to know about a property.

Then you have large corporations with vast portfolios of properties—they don't necessarily want their properties' information out in public. Public access will affect their sales and rents. It will also require additional manpower to produce all the documents and build an infrastructure for people to readily access that information.

You end up in a fight between these two powers. However, this isn't unique to the property industry. For years, the sugar industry used its lobbyists to push for not having to inform consumers of the exact content of sugar in products. There has always been a gridlock between those who want to share knowledge with the public and those who want to keep it hidden because they benefit from that lack of disclosure.

Conclusion

The several-thousand-year-old pyramids still stand because the only technology they had was nature and as such, they had no windows, air conditioning or modern technological comforts to contend with. 200 years ago, buildings were designed and built with a solid brick structure that had no reinforcing steel inside and many still stand to this day. Through the years, increased desire for human comfort and technological advances have resulted in the need for more and more maintenance to prolong buildings' useful lifespan. Modernizations such as mechanical and electrical systems add to the complexity and expense for maintenance. Steel reinforcement allows for aesthetic larger window openings which are also ways for water to get into the building, thus increasing the propensity for a building to deteriorate at a much faster pace.

Even as late as the 1930s, building structures were built to last. Many people think that 9-11 marked the only time a large airplane crashed into a New York building. But in 1945, a B-25 bomber crashed into the Empire State Building. It happened when an Army pilot made a bad turn in heavy fog. Fourteen people were killed, but the building was opened the following Monday with no major structural damage having occurred. On the other end of the spectrum today, Wal-Mart intentionally designs its buildings to last fifteen to twenty years, following the retail industry's need to adapt to modern changes in the marketplace. In short, the focus of building structures and homes in the modern era is not so much to have them last, but to conform to the buyers' needs for comfort and an easy sale.

Although the first recorded traces of the adoption of the condominium form of tenure dates back to first-century Babylon, it was only as recently as 1958 when the United States passed its first condominium law in the Commonwealth of Puerto Rico. Therefore, it has been approximately sixty years that condominium laws have been in place that govern the behaviors of residents, managers, and board members. As has been concluded in this book, these are the same behaviors that have contributed to not only the Champlain Towers collapse, but many of the other accidents and tragedies of the past, and likely those that are yet to occur. It just so happens that sixty years is also the lifespan of the typical building, which in many cases, in an over-simplified analogy, is similar to our own human longevity. So just imagine what the future has in store for us should new laws and regulations fail to be enacted for all those condominiums as they age past their useful life without proper and timely inspections, maintenance, repairs, and support mechanisms to pay for them.

Just as many other civilizations before us did when they suffered a calamity with their buildings, we must also learn from these tangible flaws and legislative short-comings. As discussed in the early chapters of this book, hundreds of generations before us learned the hard way, by trial-and-error, to build better and safer buildings through the instituting of codes and laws so that layers of responsibility are baked into the system.

There are several recommendations I would make to the legislators, building officials, residents and other stake-holders. These are as follows:

First of all, I would recommend that the laws be altered so that reserve studies be mandated and in compliance with national standards without giving an option to opt-out (as is currently the case in Florida), and the information should be accessible to all interested parties such as future home buyers. Also, the money in the reserves should only be used for purposes that they are intended for. Although community rules and regulations are largely governed by state law, Florida laws currently fall short. There is no practical reason why laws cannot be passed that help fix this problem, and this can ultimately serve as an example to other states that are also in dire need of implementing reforms. This holds true for a nation whose political dysfunction has led our future generations to be among those that inherit a massive deteriorating infrastructure problem, and thus are left to suffer the lethal consequences of inaction.

During the writing of this book, I was surprised to learn that Florida had enacted such a law in 2008, only for it to be repealed by the Florida Legislature in 2010! Julio Robaina, a Republican congressman, had sponsored the law that included a requirement that condo associations hire engineers to estimate the cost of repairs in five-year intervals. It is of note that state Representative Gary Aubuchon, a real estate broker and homebuilder, sponsored the bill's repeal. Mr. Robaina blames the bill's demise on industry push-back and that the property management and owner costs were too high to maintain a condo.

As an engineer, I find this vexing. We have been entrusted to protect the public safety at all costs. At the core of what we do, day in and day out, is the mantra that we will design buildings so that people should not have to think twice about the structural integrity of a condo when visiting, buying, or renting it. Why would democratically-elected representatives of the people think any differently?

As a contractor and real estate investor, I personally find this offensive and troubling at best. When one invests money or sweat equity in a property, one has the professional and moral obligation to ensure that the people that inhabit these spaces are in a safe and secure environment, even in the face of significant maintenance expenses and regulations.

I understand that the topic of reserve studies and allocating funds is exceptionally complicated, and to provide further details and recommendations would be beyond the scope of this book. I'd like to add that the CAI (Community Association Institute) conducted a survey in 2020 that concluded that most associations are hesitant to require additional fees because they will expect opposition from other residents. This equates to allowing associations to kick the can down the road in states that allow it. Thus, the extremely thorny maze for fixing this funding issue will certainly be a challenge to navigate for current and future lawmakers.

Personally, I do not believe that today we have the political will and rationality to enact real laws that will help alleviate this affliction. However, I do hold out hope that the private sector (such as mortgage, financial, and insurance companies), in protecting itself, will begin requiring inspections and insist on tougher reserve fund rules. Hopefully, the market forces will eventually dictate this.

Acknowledging these challenges of the political environment, I'll transition my focus toward recommending some low-hanging-fruit solutions. Regular inspections are at the top of the list. In Florida, we have the 40-year recertification inspection where buildings in South Florida (Dade and Broward counties) are inspected upon reaching their 40th birthday and every ten years thereafter. Having done hundreds of 40-year inspections, it is my opinion that they play an important role in ensuring that consequent repairs are made in older buildings. I would also recommend that the 40-year recertification process in Florida be further solidified by making the mandated inspections on a 30-year cycle instead of the 40-year regular cycle, particularly for properties close to the ocean.

Reserve studies, although not the same as an engineering inspection, are reports that are made to forecast expenditures for repairs and replacement of many building components such as paint, mechanical and electrical equipment, structure, and driveways. This important report lets the stakeholders know how to save and budget for repairs, replacement, and maintenance costs in the years to come so that they have available funds when needed.

Only a handful of states have a reserve study requirement, and Florida is not one. On the other hand, there are another handful of states that do not have any statutory guidance or the requirement for a reserve study.

The next low-hanging fruit I'd like to recommend is vigilance on the part of residents, property managers, owners, and others that regularly interact with the building. Legislation, building departments, rules, and regulations can only do so much. The people living at the building are at the front lines. These folks have a massive responsibility for taking care of their residences not only for themselves, but for the common good. The board members entrusted to manage these associations carry the extraordinary burden of ensuring that the residents live in a safe environment. With that said, I urge the unit owners and board members to have a basic understanding of their buildings and the need for proper care and maintenance. Reading books like this one or even accessing the Internet on any engineering, construction, or maintenance subject will work wonders, even if just to identify a potential problem. These folks should also have the resources and knowledge to reach out to the right experts. I firmly believe that a seemingly insignificant dose of timely attention will go a long way to averting disaster at a building.

This brings me to the next recommendation of painting. Although performing a periodic paint job is not on the "low-hanging fruit" list, it is the cheapest way to avoid expensive, long-term structural problems like spalling and water intrusion. When I mention "painting" it should include caulking replacement, crack sealing, weatherstripping, and waterproofing susceptible areas. If a regular paint and waterproofing job had been performed at Champlain Towers, this accident likely would not have occurred. I recommend that coastal condominiums be painted every seven to ten years, and the building should be reviewed by an engineer at the same time, since it will conveniently be covered in hanging scaffolds.

In my opinion, painting a building is more of a maintenance item than it is an aesthetic one. At its core, a thorough paint job protects and substantially increases a building's longevity. Many think of maintenance as an expense. The reality is that there is an actual pay-back in the form of a substantial decrease in repairing future problems. The cost of maintenance can seem super-fluous when a building is running smoothly. Over time, systems will inevitably run more inefficiently and regular wear and tear will take their toll. And if not kept up in a timely manner, the building will become a dangerous and unhealthy environment for its residents and visitors. Industry research has shown that regular maintenance reduces breakdowns by up to 70%, reduces down time by up to 45%, lowers repair and emergency maintenance costs by up to 30%, and even reduces energy consumption by 5% to 20%.

The single most important lesson Champlain Towers has taught us is that the best thing any board member, property manager, owner, or resident can do to keep a building safe and running in an efficient manner is to properly maintain the building. The scope of a building's maintenance ranges from simple checklists performed by local personnel to reviewing electrical and security logs. It includes taking the time to make sure that the equipment manufacturing maintenance regiments are followed, such as replacing filters, oils, and belts. These days, many building systems are run by computers (ventilation and A/C, security, fire alarms, computer cabling, motion sensors, elevators, etc.) and as such, one needs to ensure that the software is up to date, working properly, and those in charge understand its upkeep. These are just a few of the many more items that need to be monitored and maintained. For larger buildings, this upkeep is a full-time job which at times requires a team of experienced professionals if it is to be done correctly.

For smaller buildings that do not have a budget to have full-time help, a good starting point will be to determine the building's capacity to pay for current and future maintenance expenditures. Perform a reserve study by hiring a local professional. If the building is smaller and there is no reserve study, it is advisable to gather documentation about the equipment and systems the building has, and make a list of items that need maintenance. A quick conversation with a professional property manager, contractor, or engineer will go a long way. Other companies will even visit the site and provide a list.

According to Ray Dalio, my favorite billionaire-investor and educator, it is an established certainty that the USA is in decline as a new world order continues to take shape. He mentions that one of the many indicators of a declining US is its failing infrastructure and our dereliction of duty to invest in its longevity and modernization. Florida is typically the butt of jokes on late-night shows for its crazy stories, inability to handle situations, and what Trevor Noah jokingly called "America's flaccid penis." I love my home state of Florida. I've brought up a beautiful family here, it's where I have my successful business, and it is where I will likely take my last breath. Unfortunately, the Champlain Towers collapse has helped add gasoline to the fire of Florida's regrettable reputation. With this backdrop, I feel that Florida has the unique opportunity to take a leading role in condo safety and infrastructure investment reform in the USA by educating the public and enacting reasonable rules and regulations for the betterment of our collective well-being and safety.

Introduction to the Basics of Concrete Repair

As an expert witness, I have written hundreds of reports for clients and court cases; the style and language I use in those technical reports are very professional since they are intended for other engineers, judges, and lawyers. On the other hand, this book is written for the non-engineer types who want to be informed about a seemingly simple topic but, in actuality, is very complex.

In all the years of performing engineering, construction, and inspections for concrete repairs, I have often dealt with people who ask themselves, "why do I have to spend all this money to repair concrete?", "why is it so important?", "why was this not repaired years ago?" These are all extremely valid questions and ones that I must answer time and time again. It's my job as an engineer to educate my clients because an educated and informed client is the best client. Having an open dialogue prompts trust, and without trust, the job eventually becomes unnecessarily more difficult for all parties.

The stereotypical engineer is a person who is rigid in personality and lacks that caring nature we often see in teachers or nurses. I consider myself the opposite. I place a lot of weight on the role I take as instructor and partner. I love to talk to people, take care of their issues and solve problems for them. That's why I became an engineer. I am not interested in sitting in front of a computer all day, juggling formulas, and cranking out plans. I love interacting with people and helping them arrive at the best possible solutions to their problems.

Put yourself in my shoes for a second. When I get a call to be involved in a concrete repair project, I am automatically confronted with a group of people with differing opinions. Some insist that the repair work must be done, some think it is unnecessary, and others have varying opinions on everything in between. A lack of knowledge and, at times, denial of the issue is the fuel that drives unnecessary confrontations between owners, boards, property managers, and the residents (who are the ones who end up paying the bills by way of loans and assessments). As an engineer in the concrete repair business, my first enemy is not concrete corrosion. It is the lack of education on this topic.

In this role, I have taken it upon myself to produce videos, write books, and teach, and then let the informed masses make the decisions that best suit them. My experience has taught me that an informed client makes better decisions. Hopefully, this appendix will be helpful to you. This informative and practical discussion will not replace the reasonable judgment of an experienced engineer or contractor, nor will it help you deal with the almost infinite number of issues that will arise during your repair process. Instead, this content aims to put you in a position where you and those you hire will start on the right path and hopefully remain on the same wavelength. Otherwise, your project is well on its way to becoming an emotional and financial disaster.

I must also mention that this book is in no way meant to give legal advice. At a minimum, you should always hire a lawyer whenever there is a contract on the table or you have legal questions.

What is concrete spalling?

Florida and Florida's coast: beautiful beaches, impeccable weather, and an all-around great place to live. However, these positive attributes do not come without their share of specific problems. The high concentrations of corrosive agents that are present in the atmosphere are especially problematic in coastal climates such as ours. These naturally occurring substances seep into the concrete of coastline structures and start rusting the steel reinforcement grid that acts as a support inside the concrete. This phenomenon can eventually render the entire structure dangerous and can progress into a state of disrepair that is possibly life-threatening. Although the corrosion process is more complex, this appendix provides a simplified explanation for those who aren't technically inclined. This picture shows what a typical spall

EXPOSED REINFORCING STEEL

looks like. The classic spall is one where you remove the loose and cracked concrete, and the reinforcing steel is exposed.

When the original contractor installs the steel reinforcement inside the concrete during the initial construction of the building, it is in pristine and non-rusted condition. That steel has a protective finish layer that is called the "passivation layer." But coastal atmospheres contain a high concentration of salts (chlorides) that seep into the porous concrete. When these chlorides permeate the concrete, they damage the passivation layer, causing the steel to rust and expand.

If you live near the coast, you've likely observed multiple examples of this process in action without even realizing it. You've likely seen cracks or portions of the concrete that is ready to break free from buildings. These are just a couple of examples of this process in action. When you strike the concrete with a hammer, the rusted steel reinforcement, or "rebar," is easily exposed. The technical term for this cracking of the concrete is "spalling." These spalling cracks indicate that the reinforcing steel (rebar) is rusting and must be repaired for your structure to remain intact and, more importantly, safe.

Concrete has been used for thousands of years in various forms. The Romans built magnificent concrete structures that survive today, such as the Pantheon, with its impressive concrete dome. However, the Pantheon does not need any reinforcing steel because of its design. The dome's concrete was always compressed under its own weight. Concrete by itself, without any steel rebar inside of it, can withstand a tremendous amount of this compressive force. On the other hand, concrete cannot resist a large amount of tensile force, which pulls it apart. As domes are less relevant in the modern design era, the structures we build today, from traditional homes to high-rise condos, are subjected to tensile and compressive forces. Around the turn of the century, engineers noticed that if you included reinforcing steel inside the concrete, it could withstand a tremendous amount of

both tensile forces and compressive forces. This meant that one could now design and build structures without being hindered by concrete's structural limitations. This is how the era of building modern concrete structures began. Without steel in your concrete to support the structure, you would not have a soundly-built building. The reinforcing steel, or "rebar," inside the concrete keeps your entire structure from crumbling.

It is important to note that not all cracks in the concrete indicate spalling. An engineer will perform the appropriate testing to determine if it is spalling and, if so, the severity. The seriousness of a spall has everything to do with the size and the location of the damage. It can be in a column, in the slab, on a beam, or inside the property itself. Although falling pieces of concrete can cause injury and damage to property, it is not the most dangerous concern.

The real danger is much more insidious. As the reinforcing steel weakens, the concrete structure weakens as well. If the problem is left unattended, the concrete structure will eventually collapse, resulting in severe damages to the building. It could threaten the lives of those in proximity to the building, as occurred at Champlain Towers in Surfside. This is why all of the coastal cities in South Florida, from Boca Raton to the Keys, instituted a permitting process where these damages are identified, classified, documented, submitted, approved for repairs, and ultimately performed. Check with your local building regulation agency for their specific process of performing structural repairs.

At this critical juncture, an engineer is vital since it is the engineer who will guide you and provide invaluable expertise through the entire repair process. While the process is intricate, the following basic nine steps will provide you with a simplified way of staying the course. Please note that these steps are provided to the reader to oversimplify an extremely complex process so that you can understand and hopefully be on the same wavelength as the professionals you hire.

Overview of steps

STEP 1: Choose your engineer. Refer to Appendix B in this book titled "Hiring an Engineer" for more detailed information on this crucial step.

STEP 2: Your engineer will identify, classify, and quantify the different types of concrete damages present. The repair cost projection varies depending on the location and severity of the damage. We will call this the "Quantification" document.

STEP 3: The engineer compiles another set of documents called the "Plans and Specifications," which are the instructions to the contractor on how to perform the repairs. This can be in the form of a large set of plans, a letter-sized document, or both. The Quantifications are included in these Plans and Specifications.

STEP 4: The engineer can assist you in putting together a "Bid Package," which will give specific instructions to the prospective bidding contractors on how to put together their bid and when to submit it. This Bid Package will contain the Plans and Specifications and any other documents that the contractor will need to put a proposal together that can be compared apples-to-apples with the other bids.

STEP 5: Choose a contractor, negotiate a contract, and sign the contract.

STEP 6: A permit for construction is applied for with your local Building Department.

STEP 7: Obtain the Permit from your Building Department.

STEP 8: The contractor starts and performs the repairs.

STEP 9: Perform maintenance to protect your investment.

Before Step 1: A prologue

Before we begin the very first and critical step, it is essential to mention that not all cracks in the concrete require that you hire an engineer. Cracking can be caused by many other factors, such as delaminating stucco, which is stucco that has separated from the concrete beneath, or superficial surface cracking.

The first step in correctly diagnosing the cause of a crack is to use a hammer on the concrete to remove the hollow stucco (or suspected spall). If the underlying concrete does not contain any cracking, you must remove the remaining loose plaster and patch it. Depending on the amount of stucco to be removed and replaced, you probably don't need to hire a contractor nor pull a permit to complete this repair. Of course, it is always best to call your local Building Department to confirm this. It's that simple.

Unfortunately, many lay people mistakenly diagnose serious concrete repairs as stucco repairs. They are often in denial or are unwilling to pay for a proper structural repair. They proceed to remove the stucco or loose concrete and patch over the hole without taking the appropriate measures to remedy the critical problem of the corroding steel issue. This is the worst-case scenario. Patching up the affected area is merely a cosmetic fix, and the steel rebar continues to weaken and becomes increasingly unstable as time wears on. By the time the cracking reappears (and with certainty, it will reappear), it will have spread much farther into the concrete and will require a more extensive and expensive repair. The adage of "a stitch in time saves nine" certainly applies here.

The onset of corrosion in the steel rebar is to a building what cancer is to a human. The disease spreads undaunted if left unattended. Cancer patients have to undergo chemotherapy and other treatments to abate the disease; similarly, there is one severe course of action when dealing with buildings' spalling "disease." The only 100% effective way to remedy this "reinforcing steel cancer" is through direct surgical removal of the corroded areas, which is very technical and requires quality control and inspections (by your engineer).

It is also important to note that the procedure as outlined in this appendix is geared toward projects that are larger in scope. For example, you will not necessarily need an in-depth screening of engineers and contractors if you will only be commissioning repairs for one or two small spalled areas.

Let's begin by enumerating and explaining each step in more detail. Bear in mind that the enumeration of these steps is a basic guide to instruct the reader and is not intended to be used as a strict template to follow for each project. It is essential to understand that more extensive projects, such as high-rise buildings, must go through each step while smaller projects, such as single-family homes, can customize the steps in a way that best suits them. The engineer that you hire will be the person to guide you through the steps in a way that is tailored specifically to your project.

Step 1: Choose your engineer

As a big basketball fan, I compare your engineer to a basketball team's head coach. The coach teaches and advises the team members on the best approach to competing and presents and implements a plan to ensure ultimate victory.

It is imperative to bring in your coach at the very beginning of the repair process. Why? Your engineer is a professional that is experienced and qualified to help you through all the steps. This is particularly important, considering that a licensed engineer should perform the initial steps. Choosing the right engineer is critical to the success of your restoration project.

You could employ a reputable, competent, and experienced contractor to inspect the building and provide an assessment of the quantities to repair. This contractor can also give you a price and in the end, may not even charge you for the estimate. I have often seen people hire a contractor before they hire an engineer. This is absolutely the wrong way to go about it—you are putting the cart before the horse.

Contractors may advise you not to go with an engineer first. Let it be known that I am both an engineer and a contractor and am not biased either way. Let me explain why hiring a contract first is a mistake. First and foremost, the contractor's quantification will not be valid for submission of the plans to the city (i.e., for permitting) unless it is signed and sealed by an engineer. No reasonable engineer is careless enough to sign off on a quantification that a contractor performs without the engineer's direct involvement. Doing so violates Florida Law and is punishable by the Florida Board of Professional Engineers. I'm not saying that contractors are not qualified; I know many contractors that can perform this work just as well as, and at times even better than, some engineers with a license can. This is not the point. The point is that if you are going to pull a permit to perform these repairs (and in 99.9% of cases, you must), then all the documentation relating to the quantities, methods of repair, plans, and specifications must be signed and sealed by a licensed engineer to be accepted by your Building

Department. If a contractor performs this work for you, it will likely be a colossal waste of time for him since the inspection will have to be re-done by the engineer.

Choosing the right engineer doesn't have to be a grueling task. A written proposal to complete the job should suffice as a tool to compare candidates to each other. You should ask them to affix the following information:

- Past project
- References
- Qualifications
- Copies of their licenses
- Insurance information (Errors & Omissions insurance)

Many condo associations have found it helpful to ask the engineers to talk to the board and introduce themselves and answer questions on the spot. But you must keep in mind that the engineer's cost is typically a fraction of the eventual cost of the repairs. All your energy should not be focused on hiring the right engineer, but on analyzing the much higher cost of construction and hiring a reputable and competent contractor.

Appendix B covers hiring an engineer in more depth, and I encourage you to read it as you begin your search. Also, I have compiled the following checklist as a guide for those seeking an engineer for their concrete repair project:

Checklist To Choose Your Engineer

_____ Professional Engineer License Number. Confirm if the license is valid with your state's Engineering Licensing Board, and you can even check if this engineer has had any prior record of violating rules or regulations.

_____ If you live in Florida, you can obtain a Certificate of Authorization from the Florida Board of Professional Engineers. To offer engineering services in Florida under an Association, Fictitious name, Partnership, Corporation, or LLC, the business entity must hold a Certificate of Authorization under Florida Statute Section 471.023.

_____ Years of experience in concrete repair.

$_____ Amount of E&O (Errors & Omissions) Insurance. Also known as Professional Liability Insurance. This covers the engineer (and thus the owners) from mistakes or omissions made in the normal course of the work. $1 million policy coverage is typical for established firms.

$_____ Amount of General Liability Insurance. If your engineer is performing inspections on the project, the engineer (and consequently, the owner) should protect himself from liability in the event of property damage or bodily injury. $1 million to $2 million is the norm for an established firm.

_____ Intangibles. Insist on meeting the licensed engineer in person and any person to whom he will delegate your project. Rate your engineer on his communication and interpersonal skills. Is the engineer approachable and accessible? Does the engineer exude the leadership, respect, and confidence needed to lead the team? You can have the best technical engineer in the world, but if that person is inaccessible, uncommunicative, or unapproachable, you don't have much.

_____ Rate your engineer on how directly involved he will be with your project. For example, is he going to delegate to subordinates? If so, to whom will he delegate? Obtain information on these people also.

_____ Amount of technical staff to perform the work (including required inspections) when the project requires it.

Does the engineer have an established physical office? Yes ____ No ____. For how long have they had this office? _____

_____ Has the engineer ever been sued or have any legal claims been made against him or the company regarding his duties as an engineer? Are there any current and pending claims?

Past project references:
Reference #1:   Name: _____
Contact Information: _____

Reference #2:   Name: _____
Contact Information: _____

Reference #3:   Name: _____
Contact Information: _____

_____ Does your engineer also have hands-on experience in concrete repair as a contractor, and is he someone who can bring that dimension of experience to the table when performing the engineering facet of the project?

Memberships in associations related to the concrete repair industry:
1. _____

2. _____

3. _____

4. _____

Leadership positions or professional organizations (is the engineer respected in his field?):

1. _____

2. _____

3. _____

4. _____

Checklist notes:

_____

_____

_____

_____

Keep in mind that the cost of an engineer is a small fraction of what your construction costs are going to be, so make your primary focus on hiring the right contractor and helping your engineer stave off issues before they happen.

This checklist is to be used only as a guide to help you choose the right engineer and to empower you to ask the right questions of those you are looking to hire.

Step 2: Classify and quantify

Now that you have your engineer on board, the next step is to identify, classify, and quantify the amount of concrete that requires repair.

The engineer must scour the building in search of areas of concern that must then be categorized and quantified. These quantities are critically important to the prospective contractors who will provide you with a price to perform each type of repair. Finally, the engineer compiles a document with the quantities and classifications and indicates the materials to be used and the methods for repair.

Typically, these plans and specifications are critical for two reasons: 1) They will be sent to the competing contractors to bid on the same quantities and methods of repair so that the different quotes can be compared on an apples-to-apples basis and, 2) these documents will be submitted to the city by the winning contractor so they can pull a permit to start the repairs.

The importance of classifying the concrete repairs is that each different repair class requires a different set of skills and materials. As such, the bidding contractors will set different prices for each class of repair and will provide you with an all-encompassing price once they are given the complete quantities and classifications of the concrete repairs.

Let's look at some fundamental and common types of repairs:

Balcony Edge Spall

The picture above illustrates a balcony edge spall that is currently undergoing repair. You can see where the contractor has already chipped out the concrete and has exposed the rusted steel underneath. Balcony edge spalls are common because the edges are the most exposed to the elements. There is a specific method of repair to remedy spalling in this area. These repairs are typically measured and quantified by the Linear Foot (LF).

Beam Spall

A beam spall is one of the more severe spalls because a concrete beam is designed to support the loads of other structural members. If a beam structurally fails, then all the other structural members that it was supporting will most likely also fail. Beam repairs are typically quantified and measured by the Cubic Foot (CF).

Column Spalls

Because columns always support other structures above them, these spalls are also severe and should be repaired once they are discovered. Contractors take special precautions in performing these repairs since they must provide temporary support (or "shoring")

to the surrounding areas to prevent them from failing while the repairs are being performed. Your engineer is the person who will strategically place these shores. Column repairs are quantified and measured by the Cubic Foot (CF).

Ceiling Spalls

Ceiling spalls are dangerous because falling pieces of concrete could cause injury or damage to property. If left unrepaired, these balconies or catwalks will eventually collapse. Ceiling spalls are quantified and measured by the Square Foot (SF) and typically are more expensive to repair due to the difficulty involved in fixing them. Please note that ceiling spalls can be sub-categorized as a "partial depth" repair and also as a "full depth" repair. The picture above shows a partial depth repair in progress. At times, the spalling on the ceiling is so severe that the chipping of the concrete goes through the entire slab. When this occurs, the contractor must take a completely different approach to repair the area (and thus, the unitary price to repair will likely increase from the initial quote). This is why many engineers, upon performing their repair survey, distinguish between a "partial-depth" and a "full-depth" repair. The fact remains, however, that it is virtually impossible for an engineer to accurately define these quantities without X-Ray vision. I will expand more on this issue later in this appendix.

Floor Spalls

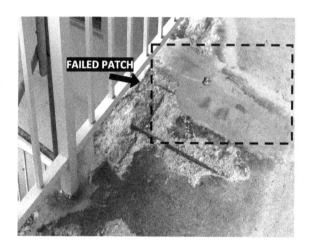

Floor spalls are more accessible to repair than ceiling spalls. You will note in the picture that someone has already taken the time to perform a patch job that did not work. If this patch had been performed correctly to begin with, this slab would not be in this state of disrepair today. To make matters worse, the owner will now have to pay twice for the same repair.

Other Spalling Issues You'll Probably Run Across

Electrical metal conduit also rusts and causes spalling. If you look closely at the picture, you will see that a portion of the electrical conduit has been replaced with a new conduit. It is good to have an electrician handy when performing concrete repairs due to accidental cuts to the electrical lines.

Your engineer must classify each type of repair because it is important for your prospective bidders to know the nuances of your concrete repair to provide you with proper pricing. Your engineer must also quantify each type of spall in tandem with the classification. When a contractor knows the kind of spall and the total quantity of that spall in the building, they can arrive at a total price to perform the repair. For example, if the engineer determines that the entire building contains 555 Linear Feet of edge spalls, the contractor then multiplies this number by how much he can perform this work for (or unit price). For this example, the unitary price is $100 per Linear Foot.

555 Linear Feet X $100/Linear Foot = $55,500

Thus, as the formula above has illustrated, the contractor will quote $55,500 to repair all the edge spalling in this building. Of course, there are column, beam, floor, and ceiling spalls and a host of other items. Later in this appendix, I will discuss this pricing process in more detail.

It should suffice to say for now that the classification and quantification performed by the engineer is critical for a couple of reasons:

- It provides the essential information to be included in the Plans and Specifications submitted to the city to obtain a permit.

- It gives the contractors the needed information so they can correctly price the job and give you a more accurate project cost.

To ensure a job well done, the engineer must inspect the entire building looking for instances of spalling. An experienced professional should have a knack for finding these spalls. However, even the most experienced engineers do not have x-ray vision. To find a spall is one thing, but to quantify it is an entirely different matter. The repair method requires that the contractor "chase" the reinforcing steel until they find "clean" rebar, which can be difficult in certain situations.

Sample quantification and unit pricing from a contractor

The table on the next page is a sample of a quantification for a repair performed some time ago. I have purposely removed the actual quantities and drastically changed the unit price numbers. However, several items should be noted:

- Not all projects are the same. The size of the list may vary significantly from building to building depending on items such as the scope of work required by the owner, the state of deterioration the building is in, and the judgment and experience of the engineer.

- Once your engineer compiles the list of repairs, he can also provide you a budget number for these repairs if they are so qualified.

GREG BATISTA, PE

ALLINGTON TOWERS BID SHEET

CONCRETE REPAIR QUANTIFICATION & ESTIMATE
Page 1 of

	Quantity	UNIT	Unit Price	Amount
Floor Spall Parital Depth (SF)	10	SF	$ 10.00	$ 100.00
Ceiling Spall Partial Depth(SF)	20	SF	$ 10.00	$ 200.00
Column Spall (CF)	30	CF	$ 10.00	$ 300.00
Balcony Edge Spall (LF)	10	LF	$ 10.00	$ 100.00
Spalling below window (LF)	20	LF	$ 10.00	$ 200.00
Spalling below Sliding Glass Door (LF)	30	LF	$ 10.00	$ 300.00
Ceiling Spalling at interior of unit (SF)	10	SF	$ 10.00	$ 100.00
Spalling at Wall (SF)	20	SF	$ 10.00	$ 200.00
Beam Spall (CF)	30	CF	$ 10.00	$ 300.00
Stucco Repair (SF)	10	SF	$ 10.00	$ 100.00
Wall/Ceiling/Floor Crack (LF)	20	LF	$ 10.00	$ 200.00
Post Pocket Repair at balcony Railing (EA)	30	EA	$ 10.00	$ 300.00
Post Pocket/Railing repair at Stairwells (ea)	20	EA	$ 10.00	$ 200.00
Repair Lath and Stucco at Porte Cochere	30	SF	$ 10.00	$ 300.00

OTHER RELATED ITEMS FOR BID

	Quantity	UNIT	Unit Price	Amount
Potential Full Depth Repairs (beyond 6" back from edg	10	SF	$ 10.00	$ 100.00
Ceiling Stucco Spall	20	SF	$ 10.00	$ 200.00
Rust Spot	30	EA	$ 10.00	$ 300.00
Potential Window Shutter Removal and reinstallation	81	LF	$ 10.00	$ 810.00
Potential Sliding Glass Door removal and reinstallation				
Complete Frame	10	EA	$ 10.00	$ 100.00
New Track (Material Only)	20	LF	$ 10.00	$ 200.00
Potential temporary wall at unit interior	30	LF	$ 10.00	$ 300.00
Slab Crack (rout and caulk)	10	LF	$ 10.00	$ 100.00
Ceiling Crack (rout and caulk)	20	LF	$ 10.00	$ 200.00
Leaking Ceiling Cracks (urethane or epoxy injection)	30	LF	$ 10.00	$ 300.00
Expansion Joint Repair (Urethane Caulk or Mechanica	10	LF	$ 10.00	$ 100.00
Drill and Epoxy dowels	20	EA	$ 10.00	$ 200.00
Epoxy Injection	30	LF	$ 10.00	$ 300.00
Flash Patch				
Up to 3/4"	10	SF	$ 10.00	$ 390.00
3/4" to 1-1/2"	20	SF	$ 10.00	$ 200.00
> 1- 1/2"	30	SF	$ 10.00	$ 300.00
Mobilization Cost		LS		$ 1,000.00
Permit Cost		LS		$ 1,000.00
Bond Cost (if required)		LS		1000
Other Cost:_____				$_____
Other Cost:_____				$_____
TOTAL PROJECT COST				**$ 10,000.00**

SAMPLE ONLY - ALL UNIT PRICES ARE FICTITIOUS

CONTRACTOR:
Corporate Name: G. BATISTA & ASOOCIATES
Address: 10400 GRIFFIN RD. SUITE 201, COOPER CITY, FL. 33328

Officer's Signature:
Officer's Printed Name and Title: GREG BATISTA, PRESIDENT
Date: 06/11/2012

Step 3: Plans and Specifications

"Plans and Specifications" are the documents that the contractors will use to estimate their price for the repairs. These prices will then be compared on an apples-to-apples basis to the other prospective bid prices. The "Plans" part is simply a pictorial representation of the work to be performed, while the "Specifications" is the worded description of how the work should be performed.

The Plans can contain the following items:

- A Plan View of each area to be repaired.

- An elevation drawing (side views) of the building with marks denoting where the work will occur.

The Specifications can contain the following items:

- A description of the type of materials to be used and corresponding manufacturers' information sheets describing the products, along with application methods, composition, safety precautions, etc. In particular, look for information sheets on the type of waterproofing and paint to be used.

- A written guide of the repair method and the codes to follow (Florida Building Code, ACI, ICRI, ASTM, etc.)

Step 4: Bid Package

Step 4 is to compile a third document named "Bid Sheets" or a "Bid Package." This package is important since it will be sent to your bidding contractors and will include detailed information about the damage and instructions for repair, among other things. For instance, you will want to tell your prospective contractors items such as:

- That they cannot begin work before 9 a.m.
- Parking or security arrangements.
- If they will be required to carry special insurance to work there.
- If they will be required to carry a bond for all or part of the work.
- If the project must be completed by a specific date.

These items are aspects of the job that don't necessarily have to do with the actual repairs (as is the case with the Plans and Specifications), but it is information that your bidding contractors must know upfront before providing you with a price that will more easily compare with the other bidders. Your engineer, especially one with an extensive background in construction, is critical in acting as your consultant to help you compile a thorough and complete Bid Package that makes sense to the contractors and to minimize issues and misunderstandings during the repair process

We have all our documents ... now what?

These three documents form the basis of your contract—the "Contract Documents" or "CDs":

1. The "Classification and Quantification" from Step 2 that your engineer came up with during his inspection of the structure.

2. The "Plans and Specifications" from Step 3.

3. The "Bid Sheet" from Step 4.

Now that you have compiled the CDs, you can share these documents with your bidders so that they can give you an accurate quote on a set amount of quantities and types of materials, along with the specific instructions for the repairs they are to perform.

Ensuring that you distribute the same information to all bidders is the only way you will be able to get quotes that you can then compare on the same playing field. You will be able to have the information necessary to make a more informed choice as to who your contractor will be.

I've tried to simplify this complex process into some basic steps. Don't let the straightforward way these steps are laid out lead you to believe that this is a simple process—

it's not. However, with this basic knowledge, you will be more prepared to effectively communicate with your professionals and thus face the challenges ahead. Your engineer is vital in these efforts.

Step 5: Choose a contractor

You have the bids, and now it is time to choose a contractor. Now is the time to determine whether you want your engineer involved in the decision-making process regarding choosing a contractor. Your engineer, especially one with a strong construction background, can be invaluable in helping you making an informed decision. They do this by studying the bids, helping you interview the contractors, and aiding in making the final choice. Every project is unique, and what may be a good fit for one contractor on one job may not be a good fit for another.

Choosing the right contractor for a job, especially if it is a larger project, can become a complex endeavor considering the legal, technical, logistical, and financial ramifications for the owner. This appendix serves as a basic guideline but is in no way intended to replace the experience and guidance of an attorney or engineer.

There are two critical items to look for when hiring a contractor. The first is price and the second is the contractor's *experience* and *capacity* to perform the work. The price aspect is reduced to the unit prices that the contractor provides, plus the other items that may be added. These include profit, overhead, permit costs, insurance costs, contingencies, add-alternates, etc. If you followed the previous steps as laid out in this appendix, the job should be significantly simplified because your engineer had asked your bidders to lay out the pricing so that you could compare each to the other contractors on an apples-to-apples basis. However, the task having been dramatically simplified does not necessarily mean that it is easy. Your engineer is still your best ally to effectively tie the loose ends together so that the process is cohesive. Let's face it—many contractors have tricks that they use to deflate the prices against other contractors while making it look like they comply with all the contract documents. These include:

- Adding or deleting items in the scope of work even when it is expressed in the contract documents.

- Conveniently omitting language in their bid.

- Adding language to their bid that contradicts the engineer's instructions.

- Failing to review and sign certain key documents as per the engineer's instructions.

The fact is that most contractors are reputable and want to do the right thing. If they do some of the things as expressed above, it does not necessarily make them a lousy contractor. Unfortunately, this is the way it is in this business, and the few bad contractors out there give the rest of us a bad name. This is all the more reason you should become as educated as possible on the process and seek the best professional advice.

Here are a few basic items that you should keep in mind when choosing a concrete repair contractor:

Contractor's Checklist
_____ Years of experience

_____ Does the contractor have a license as required by law?

What is the license number? _____

Whose name is it under (Qualifying Agent)? _____

_____ Is the Qualifying Agent the same person as the owner of the bidding construction company?

_____ Is the contractor insured with General Liability and Worker's Compensation as required by law? What are the limits of coverage? $_____.
Are the limits sufficient for the project? Is the insurance in the company's name or the individual that is signing the contract? _____

For more on insurance and licensing, please refer to the fraud section on page 152.

Contractor's experience.

Three names and contact numbers of previous clients and detail of the work performed (visit the job).

Name: _____ Contact Number: _____
Project Name & Address: _____
_____

Name: _____ Contact Number: _____
Project Name & Address: _____
_____

Name: _____ Contact Number: _____
Project Name & Address: _____
_____

Has the contractor visited the site and made himself familiar with the job? _____

Is the contractor bonded? _____

If so, what is the bonding capacity? $ _____

Will the contractor perform the repairs with his own forces or subcontract it out? Explain: _____
_____

Checklist notes:

_____

_____

_____

_____

Please note that "cheap" contractors tend to underbid the competition by cutting corners. When corners are cut and there is a problem on the job, the owners are left holding the bag. These contractors have a business plan to purposely bid very low to have the project awarded to them. Once they are on board, you cannot get rid of them because they already have the signed contract, and as such, they will begin looking for reasons to start producing change orders. They make money on these change orders. As an owner, this is very tough to contend with because of the difficulty of discerning whether a change order is legitimate. Whenever a contractor presents an unusually low bid, this should raise a red flag. Your engineer will help in finding out the answers you need.

An experienced engineer will have already drafted documents (the entire set of plans and Bid Documents) and forms that the contractor will review, fill out, and sign. These documents will attest to the contractor's willingness or ability to comply with the requirements needed to become a viable bidder so that the owner can seriously consider their bid when submitted. Every experienced concrete repair engineer has these forms on hand and tailors them to the requirements of each project as needed.

At this point, it is essential to remember that you may have to add in your soft costs such as permit fees, painting, extra security, tile work, or waterproofing. Your engineer who has construction experience can assist you in developing your budget in the best way possible. Study the bids, shortlist the contractors to two or three options, and then take the time to interview them in person. Often, it is a great help and a valuable asset to have one member on the board and/or committee who has some construction experience.

Once you choose a contractor, hiring an attorney to protect your interests by guiding you through the contract process is advisable. Engineers cannot dispense legal advice since it is against Florida Statute. Remember that the contract is the centerpiece of your project. The National Society of Professional Engineers (NSPE) and The American Institute of Architects (AIA) have many templates available that are widely used in the industry, and most contractors are familiar with them. Your contractor may have their own contract and you may decide to use theirs. The bottom line is that you have alternatives, but protecting yourself should be your priority.

Step 6: Submit for permit

The permitting process is when the CDs (contract documents) are submitted to the city or county to attain a construction permit. It starts when your contractor gives the contract documents to the city and ends when they give the owner the permit. You've probably heard horror stories about the permitting process in South Florida and other areas of the country, that it takes an enormous amount of time to get things done. The fact is that having an experienced engineer on your side is critical in avoiding the typical problems faced when attempting to obtain a permit. In reality, the Building Department is your friend and typically is very helpful unless they realize that you are purposely going about it the wrong way or cutting corners.

For clarity, here is the permitting process in a nutshell: Your contractor takes the contract documents to the city, where they will fill out a permit application and provide the city with more information such as a copy of their license and insurance. The plans then undergo an examination by the "structural reviewer," who is the designated engineer at the city to review and approve the contractor's permit application. Once submitted, it is out of the engineer's and contractor's hands. For smaller projects, the review process can take a couple of days. For more complex projects, the review process at the city can take a couple of weeks or even more. Items that can affect the timeline of permit issuance include the following:

- The engineer is not experienced and submits plans and specifications that are not up to par with acceptable standards.

- The contractor submits the wrong information or omits certain documents.

- The city is overwhelmed with work, and the review process is stalled.

- It is Christmastime, summertime, or any other time of year where reviewers tend to be on vacation, or they are simply part-timers.

- The contractor and/or the engineer do not follow up with the city to see if the plans are ready for pick-up after being reviewed and approved.

Step 7: Approval

After the permit is attained, the contractor can begin construction. This is not a step but a milestone. I have made this a step to signal the commencement of the job itself. Many contracts use this date as the official starting time of the job, and it's also used to establish the tentative schedule for the remainder of the project

Step 8: Perform the repairs and construction

Construction is by far the most difficult, time-consuming, and stressful part of the entire process. Concrete repairs are not cheap and are very disruptive to those living in the building. After many years of doing this, I have learned that the best way to begin the process is for the landlords, owners, associations, and condo boards to educate the residents on what concrete spalling is, the importance of repairing it, and precisely what those repairs entail. This is the main reason I produced a video documentary of the process and have authored many guides and manuals.

Realistically speaking, all of the information in this entire book will not adequately prepare you to deal with all the issues that can arise during the construction phase of the process. Every project is different and has its own unique set of challenges. This is where a competent engineer with the knowledge and experience to protect you comes in handy. The best engineer is one that not only has experience in engineering, but also in construction. Nevertheless, you should know the basics of the construction process that apply to most concrete repair projects.

If the building to be repaired is a multi-unit residence, it is an excellent idea to put something in writing and distribute it to all the unit owners and residents. It should read something like this:

South Beach Plaza Condominium

Dear Residents and Owners:

As you have probably noticed, there is a concrete problem in our building that must be repaired. Our engineers have advised us that if these items are not fixed quickly, the situation will worsen over time and eventually become a liability that risks injury and/or loss of life.

We are in the process of seeking and working with the appropriate professionals and want to let everyone at the South Beach Plaza Condominium know that there will be inconveniences while the work commences and progresses. These inconveniences will be chipping hammer noises, workers in the area, dumpsters in the parking lot, barricading for safety, among others. Although we will coordinate with these professionals to minimize the nuisance, the fact is that it will present some challenges. We currently estimate that the construction time will extend from _____ to _____, but that can change due to the nature of the work and unforeseen conditions that can arise.

We are in the process of obtaining a schedule of work. Our plan will currently consist of starting the work at the pool area, then the garage, then commencing the balcony repairs at line 1, and working toward line 20.

If you are not a resident but have tenants, please make sure they are aware of the construction activities that are to come in the near future.

Thank you for your patience and understanding while we work to ensure your absolute safety and comfort. In the end, all we want is a safe and beautiful building for all to share.

Sincerely,

Association Board President

The sounds of chipping hammers and the barricades, blocked entrances, dust, inconvenience, and cost are obvious inconveniences. But it is at these times when you have to look at the silver lining. After the repairs, your building will be a safer place to live, your property value could increase, and the building will regain its aesthetic value.

During this construction process, you will rely heavily on your engineer to ensure that all aspects of the job are done correctly. This depends on what specific services you've hired your engineer to perform, such as inspectors, construction consultants, a project manager, or an owner's representative. Whatever the case may be, this is the basic run-down of how projects are typically set up in South Florida. Other states will be a little different, but the basics of the process hold true.

For example, Florida will require that the owner hire a "special inspector" for the project. The special inspector is a person who will act as the project's inspector (not to replace the city's inspections) that will sign off on the project at the end by providing the city with a signed and sealed letter attesting that the project was performed in accordance with the Plans and Specifications. This special inspector is key because he makes sure that the job is done correctly. Most of the time, the engineer you hired is also the special inspector, but that is not always the case. Again, this is how inspections are coordinated in South Florida and will likely vary from jurisdiction to jurisdiction.

Before I get carried away in explaining more about the inspection processes, you must understand that concrete repair work includes several steps that require inspections along the way. Your engineer is the person who is typically responsible for monitoring the job and making sure everything is being done accurately. You see, concrete repairs are not just a quick "chip-out and patch."

There is a very specific and technical methodology for these repairs, and strict quality control is required by the special inspector, as well as by the city and/or county inspectors. It is the special inspector's responsibility to ensure that this methodology is followed. Certain basic and critical steps must be taken for a proper concrete ·repair. The special inspector must inspect each step along the way because, at the end of the project, the city will require that the special inspector certify the work was completed properly through a written certification letter. Let's take a look at the very basic repair process.

As an example, we have a concrete slab that has a corroded portion of rebar and a portion of rebar that is in pristine condition. The contractor must chip out the concrete surrounding the spalled area and chase it until he sees un-rusted rebar. This "chasing" is where a lot of problems originate. The engineer does not have x-ray vision when performing their original concrete inspection and quantification. There is no way they can precisely foresee the exact amount of concrete to be removed. The engineer goes primarily by judgment and experience to estimate this amount. It is only when the contractor takes a chipping hammer to the concrete that the exact amount that needs to be repaired can be adequately assessed. This becomes a big problem because most contracts are based on a unit cost, such as $100/sf of chipped concrete or $60/lf of chipped concrete. If the corrosion is worse than anticipated, your budget will be less reliable in terms of the bottom line. Hiring an experienced engineer and adding some contingency plans into the project are just a couple of things you can do to minimize the impact of possible overruns.

After the contractor chases the rebar, they proceed to clean the rusted rebar by any approved means like utilizing a wire wheel or sandblasting. Sometimes the rusting has eaten away at so much of the rebar that it requires complete replacement (that's up to your engineer to determine). The bottom line is that the more you wait to repair it, the more corrosion builds up, and the more expensive the repair process gets.

Your contractor then paints the exposed and clean surface of the rebar with an anti-corrosive material to protect it from continued corrosion. These chemicals are expensive, but they are applied to protect your repair investment.

Finally, the contractor replaces the concrete over the rebar and the repair is complete.

When the contractor chips out the concrete, an inspection takes place by the city and the special inspector. Several more inspections occur before your contractor is finally approved to cover up the rebar with concrete. Depending on your jurisdiction, each time the engineer performs an inspection, the engineer must make a report approving (or disapproving) the work that has been performed. The contractor can replace the concrete only if the aforementioned report by your engineer is completed and approved. As previously mentioned, the engineer generates a report that he will provide to the Building Department so they will be updated as to the progress of the project, and then he provides the final certification when the repairs are completed at the end of the project.

Once the project is completed

Once the repair process has been completed, two often-overlooked items should be noted:

First, the contractor must close out the permit, and you must receive a document from the contractor stating this. Closing out the permit is a final step that the contractor must take. This action signals to the city that the project is officially over. If the contractor does not do this, the city will believe that the permit is still active and will be waiting for the contractor's call for inspections. As a result, the permit remains in limbo until someone at the Building Department notices and requires that you, as the owner, close it. By that time, the contractor is possibly unavailable or not interested in doing this since he has already been paid. There are all sorts of issues that surface if this last step is not taken with the presiding jurisdiction. Ask the contractor to provide you with this closing document from the city before final payment.

Second, get a written warranty of the repairs with a start date and end date. The warranty terms should have been clarified at the beginning of the project in your contract.

You must educate your residents, have reputable professionals on board, as well as an acceptable contract set up with a decent contractor; this way, you are on the right path to making this entire process less painful than it otherwise could be.

Step 9: Maintenance

If your building is located in a coastal environment, concrete damage is a maintenance issue. This is not an opinion but a fact. Time and time again, I have seen residents and owners ignoring the tell-tale signs of spalling out of inexperience, denial, or both. The reality is that you don't have to be an engineer to know that you have a concrete problem. However, if it is ignored, it will become more severe and much more expensive to repair. My recommendation is to have an inspection performed every one to five years to monitor the condition of your building and detect any issues early.

Now that you are familiar with the basics, I will address costs. Concrete repairs can be very costly. This is the kind of issue that is best taken care of immediately after detection. The worst thing you can do is kick the can down the road. This is what occurred at Champlain Towers. It is ultimately a safety issue and absolutely must be done correctly by experienced professionals if you want to ensure the best possible outcome.

Repairs that are not performed by professionals only provide a cosmetic fix that will not get rid of the underlying corrosion (or, as I often refer to in this book, as "cancer") that will only worsen over time. Chances are that you will be paying for the repair twice if done the first time incorrectly.

Your engineer can estimate the financial impact of your job after they do their quantification, but the actual cost will not be known until you get your contractors' bids. And even after getting your contractors' bids, unforeseen conditions could render your initial budget obsolete. Your engineer is your best ally in this quest for attaining the best guess at a budget.

Preventing corrosion

The first defense against steel corrosion in concrete is the original contractor who built the project. For starters, this contractor should have used a proper concrete mix and poured a sufficient amount of concrete to cover the reinforcing bars. The basic definition of "concrete cover" is that the reinforcing steel should be covered by a certain amount of concrete and not be placed too close to the surface of the concrete. Reinforcing steel placed too close to the surface tends to rust faster than steel that is not. Codes are in place (such as the ACI) so that contractors follow these rules to avoid this "burning" of the rebar close to the surface. A rebar that is less than ¾ of an inch from the surface is typically too close to the surface. A fundamental rule of thumb is that 1.5 inches is used as a cover, and it is increased in marine environments.

The quality of the concrete is also an important factor in preventing corrosion. Concrete with a water-to-cementitious material ratio (w/c) that is low enough to slow down the penetration of chloride salts and the development of carbonation is preferable. The w/c ratio should be less than 0.50 to slow the carbonation rate and less than 0.40 to minimize chloride penetration. Some codes provide limits on the maximum amount of soluble chlorides in the concrete mix.

Another ingredient for good quality concrete is air entrainment, which is basically microscopic air bubbles added to the concrete.

There are also additives in the concrete that reduce the permeability of the concrete such as silica fume, fly ash, and blast furnace slag. Corrosion inhibitors, such as calcium nitrate, act to prevent corrosion in the presence of chloride ions. In all cases, they are added to quality concrete at w/c less than or equal to 0.45. Water repellents may reduce the permeation of moisture and chlorides to a limited extent.

Other protection techniques include protective membranes, cathodic protection, epoxy-coated reinforcing bars, and concrete sealers (if reapplied every four to five years).

As you can tell, this topic can be pretty complex and is advanced for the scope of this book. You do not need to know these things in detail, but your engineer should. Concrete corrosion prevention begins at the structure's original design by way of the engineer specifying the right type of concrete before building. The responsibility then transfers to the original contractor, who is supposed to follow his design specifications by having a good quality control program in place. Ultimately, it falls upon the owners and residents of the building who must maintain thorough vigilance and provide timely repair if needed.

Fraud in the concrete repair business

To me, this is the most difficult, and at the same time, an important section to write. One of the main reasons for writing this book is to give prospective clients a tool to become as educated as possible on the process. Nothing is more effective against fraud than education. It is also written from an unbiased perspective as both a professional engineer and also as a contractor for any layperson to competently choose any engineer or any contractor and be on their way to a relatively problem-free project. Fraud in this industry comes in many forms. Let me illustrate just a few of the more common examples:

Unlicensed activity

Performing structural work without a proper contractor's license is a crime in Florida. Structural repairs are a very serious matter that cities, particularly those at the coastline, keep a watchful eye over. Improperly engineered and performed work could lead to severe property damage and potentially loss of life. Most states, especially Florida, require professionals to have a valid and active license. The mere fact that a person has a license means that the individual has complied with the requirements of obtaining one. Obtaining a license requires testing, experience, holding minimum insurance coverage, continued education, and many other factors that are there to ensure that the public is protected by certifying that a person has demonstrated a minimum capacity and competence. This kind of fraud is easy to detect and overcome. Your particular state should have easily-accessible information on contractor licenses and licensees. There should be some sort of database that will let you know if your professional is licensed, the dates of expiration, and even if there have been complaints filed in the past. A few minutes of investigation goes a long way to protecting yourself.

Fraudulent aids

It is not uncommon for a seemingly low-cost contractor to underbid the other more established companies. Why are these people much cheaper than others? The answer to this question may be because this contractor is more efficient and is very good at what they do. The answer could also be that the contractor is submitting a fraudulent bid in that they are using someone else's license, or some other anomaly. Why should you care if they are using someone else's license?

The actual license holder may not know that this person is using his license to do this work.

You will probably be signing a contract with the person who submitted the proposal, but the person (or company) whose name is on the license is a different entity. This can lead to significant headaches and legal issues if and when something goes awry on the project.

This type of fraud is easy to uncover. The only thing you must do is to ensure that the construction company and the license holder are legally "linked." When I say "linked," I mean there are certain legal entities that can be linked and not be construed as a fraud. For example, my concrete repair company's name is Real Estate Engineering, LLC, but the D/B/A is under G. Batista Engineering & Construction. If you look up my license information in Florida's myfloridalicense.com you should be able to trace it back to me, the President of the company Real Estate Engineering, LLC.

A few months ago, a client wanted me to interview a prospective bidder that had offered a very competitive price to perform the project. I called the contractor and asked him for his paperwork (license number, legal corporate name, the names of the company owners, and the name of the license holder). After digging deeper, I found that he was not only advertising himself as a contractor without a license, but the license that he was using to act as his "cover" was the license of a tile installer who knew nothing about concrete restoration. After notifying this tile installer that he is putting himself in a very precarious position just to help his supposed friend, I called the owner and told them to remove this phony contractor's bid from the list immediately. Either way, owners should make sure that they contact their engineer or attorney if they have any reservations about a company. If your engineer has already been hired to perform this analysis, you should rely on your engineer's expertise to help you sort this important task out.

Uninsured activity

Contractor insurance costs money and is typically required by law. Good contractors have it, while not-so-good contractors don't. In most states, a contractor must maintain a minimum amount of General Liability Insurance. Some roundabout contractors somehow get third parties to provide their insurance papers for them. Why should you care if they are using someone else's insurance?

- They may be using that person's insurance without their knowledge which is fraud in and of itself.

- The legal entity you will be contracting with may not be "linked" to the legal entity that holds the insurance.

If someone gets hurt on the project (or there is property damage, etc.), then your legal woes as an owner will surely deepen since the insurance is not correctly "linked" to the entity that you contracted with. The good news is that this type of fraud is easy to uncover. You simply ask for the "insurance binder" from your contractor, which should be readily available. The "insurance binder" is a sheet of paper widely used in the industry that states the company name, the insurance carrier information, and the insurance limits to inform people such as yourself of the basic insurance coverage and what type of insurances cover the contractor. You must then compare the legal entities on the binder to the legal entity on your contract, and they should match.

As a last note, cities may ask for proof of insurance, worker's compensation, or licensure as a requirement to obtaining a permit. This does not automatically mean that you shouldn't do your homework. As well-intentioned as city employees may be, cities often do not have a copy of your contract to ensure that you are contracting with the same entities. Moreover, cities know that you are the one at risk if and when things take a turn for the worse in a project due to accidents or property damage. Bottom line: you or your hired professional must complete the important task of investigating the merits of the bidders.

Board members, owners, and property managers "on the take" from contractors
They say that "the love of money is the root of all evil." Money tends to lead perfectly rational, intelligent, and

otherwise honest people to make some bad decisions. Larger concrete repair jobs are often worth millions of dollars, and the competition to acquire these jobs is fierce. Every good contractor knows that the key to being awarded a project is through marketing and influencing the people at the board or those in the position to decide which contractor to hire. Therefore, whatever influence they can exercise over these individuals provides an opening to bribery and fraud. Remember, I am both an engineer and a contractor, and I travel in these circles more than my counterparts, so I am more exposed to these instances of unethical behavior. The concrete repair business in South Florida is a small world, so the stories are widely circulated. For example, X Company losing out on the job to a "connected" but less-qualified contractor because he had bribed one of the decision-makers is not uncommon. Even as an engineer, I have been approached on more than one occasion by brazen individuals asking for money in return for a favorable review towards certain contractors during the decision-making process.

Engineer and contractor in cahoots

If you have read this book from the beginning, you will have realized that the engineer is in a position to have a say over who will be hired to perform the actual concrete repair. The owners, property managers, and board members many times depend on the engineer's judgment and experience to help them choose the right contractor for their particular job. Every good contractor knows this, and in turn, some attempt to bribe the engineers into persuading the board to choose them. There are stories of engineers, board members, and property managers that have faced stiff penalties and even jail time because they were in cahoots with the contractor. Your first line of defense in circumventing this problem is by allowing your engineer to give you a list of contractors that you should consider as well as providing your own contractor. The Internet is a great tool to search for qualified contractors, and so is the tried-and-true word-of-mouth reference.

I was been involved in a case in Broward County when I was called in to verify a contractor's invoice. The owners had previously hired a separate engineer, so my first question was "is the original engineer aware of this, and why am I being approached?" The owners were suspicious about the vast amount of repairs being billed to them and thought that it didn't seem right. After having reviewed the contracts, paperwork, and invoices, I suggested that my company check out some of the finished work to precisely quantify what had already been done and to make sure that the total invoiced amount was accurate. Our investigation revealed that the contractor was indeed over-charging the owner because the quantities on his invoices substantially surpassed the actual amount of work performed. To make matters worse, the engineer on the project had approved these invoices before payment, and was later found to have received a kickback from the contractor for a percentage of the invoices.

This type of fraud is challenging to uncover since your confidence is placed in your engineer to do the ethical thing. The best way to deal with this fraud is to have a third-party owner's representative at hand who knows about construction. This "owner's representative" can be a board member who has some construction background and can periodically check on the project. The owner's representative can also be a hired professional, although the budget will not allow hiring this person in most cases. I have written a book called *G. Batista's 1-Hour Guide to Hiring an Owner's Representative*. You can find it by visiting my website at www.askgbatista.com.

Board members, owners, and property managers "on the take" from engineers

Honestly, I have never personally heard of any engineer bribing an owner, property manager, or board member in order to garner work. I assume that the reasons for this include the fact that the budgeted money for the engineering aspect of the job is significantly less than the contracting part. Another reason may be that the ethical standards for engineers are stricter than those of a contractor, and an engineer also has much more to lose in terms of their reputation and investment in their profession if they are caught. This does not necessarily mean this type of fraud does not happen.

While it pains me to write this section, it is necessary. Corruption and bribery are everywhere in our society and the purpose of this manual is to educate the reader and minimize the chances of a wrong turn. This is a profession that I truly love and it is often tainted by unscrupulous acts that eventually give our industry a bad reputation based on the behavior of a small percentage. If you gain anything by reading this section, it should be the motivation to take time to investigate your professionals and arm yourself with a proper education on the basics of the process. Reading this book is an excellent start.

Other common issues you may run into

The repair work performed exceeds the engineer's original estimate

As explained in the previous sections, it is the engineer's job to quantify the repairs to be performed. These quantities are the basis for the plans and specifications that will be submitted to the contractors for pricing and subsequently to the Building Department to obtain a build-

GREG BATISTA, PE

ing permit. Many times these estimates are exceeded in the actual work, and the owner winds up paying the bill for the additional repairs. You must understand that quantifying concrete repairs is not like quantifying the square footage of tile to lay in your house. Your house has a fixed square footage that a contractor can accurately price. Contractors typically add an amount for contingency and waste, and eventually come up with a price that they are expected to adhere to because these tile contracts are usually based on a "lump-sum" or fixed price. Concrete repairs, on the other hand, are based on a quantity that the engineer identifies, and it could very well be inaccurate. This is not necessarily the fault of the engineer. At times, the building's corrosion problem is more pervasive than anticipated. This problem will not come to the forefront until the contractor realizes that the corrosion has reached deeper into the concrete than originally anticipated once they start chipping away at the concrete. This type of problem is more prevalent in much older buildings, especially the ones that have a history of neglect and of avoiding maintenance. This problem also tends to occur in buildings where well-intentioned but unqualified people have performed repairs and only covered the corrosion with concrete without taking care to properly remove the steel corrosion "cancer." This steel corrosion worsens under the patch job until your current contractor uncovers it. What should have been a simple concrete repair back then is now a much larger problem in the present.

Hiring an Engineer

I n this section, I am assuming that you have a serious enough problem that you would need to hire an engineer to help you diagnose and direct the repair of it. I cannot stress enough the importance of your engineer.

This section is about hiring an engineer who will eventually be at the center of your project or inspection. Choosing the wrong professional could have dire repercussions for all those involved. When I say "engineer," I am talking about a licensed engineer who has a proven track record and education, keeps up-to-date by taking required continuing education credits, and is held to a professional code of conduct and ethics.

Some things in life are relatively simple to figure out, such as making a bed or picking up a pencil. Other things start as tricky but eventually become simple once you have practiced it enough, and eventually become second nature, such as working on a computer, driving a car, or meeting new people. However, finding an engineer (or a design professional) for a project is neither easy nor is one of those things where, if you do it enough, it will become second nature. Although most property managers can competently hire an engineer during their careers for smaller projects, there will always be those technical aspects that will pose a real challenge for more extensive and complicated projects.

Most property managers and owners I know are brilliant and resourceful and have been around the block enough to hire all sorts of contractors and professionals competently. However, finding a capable, experienced, licensed, and insured engineer for a large, complicated project or inspection can be challenging, particularly when you will be receiving different proposals outlining different technical items, scopes of work, etc. After all, the engineer will be your central figure performing the inspection, providing plans, choosing contractors, and even acting as your consultant during construction.

I've spoken to many design and construction professionals all around the country, and I have concluded that

South Florida is a comparatively challenging place for engineers and contractors to conduct business. There are many reasons for this, and don't get me wrong, we have come a very long way since the days before Hurricane Andrew. The requirements imposed on the engineering and construction industry forced it to get its act together and follow rules and regulations to ensure buildings are designed and built better. The result is safer buildings.

At this point I am assuming that it is, in fact, an engineer that you need. At times, the lines between needing an engineer and needing an architect are blurry. Also, the lines can be blurred between needing an engineer when you can fulfill your needs by hiring another type of professional (such as a home inspector or contractor). By the way, my "Ask G. Batista" brand I mentioned in the Introduction was created to guide those seeking answers to these fundamental questions, and we are available to answer any questions to help you make the right decision.

Choosing the right engineer is critical to your overall success on your project. I have written this appendix as a guide so that property managers, owners, and residents may understand that there is a structured and more straightforward way of hiring an engineer, regardless of the size and breadth of your project. I would have to say, though, that if you are required to perform a simple inspection (i.e., to look at a crack that just appeared on your wall), you may not need to go through this entire process, but instead rely on Google ratings on a company, or just a friendly reference.

My genuine desire is to give you the necessary tools and information to make the best decision for you, your residents, your board, and your family.

A word of warning

First, you have to realize that there are good engineers and not-so-good ones. There are cheap engineers, and there are expensive ones. There are competent engineers, and others are not as competent. Some are insured, and some aren't. Some "engineers" even break the law by practicing engineering without being licensed. The list goes on and on. These are all matters that one must consider when choosing a professional who is so consequential to the success of your maintenance program or repair project. Selecting the wrong engineer will, at best, increase the chances of a debacle and, at worst, cost you a substantial amount of money and heartache.

Starting the search

A great place to start your quest is to search for a local engineer accustomed to dealing with your particular city or county. Also, I will assume that you don't already know an engineer that is competent, experienced, and relatively economical. I prefer that you obtain a personal reference in hiring an engineer. So, if you do not know of any engineers personally or by reference, the best way to begin your quest is by searching Google. First, you should write the keywords with what you need and the area where they should be located (i.e., "Building engineer Broward County Florida"). Then, once you click on "Search," you will get your list of results. The Internet allows the public to search for engineers by area, see the licensing information, and even obtain reviews.

Most people who don't know any better just pick up the phone and contact the first engineer they see on Google or one that someone refers to them. There isn't anything inherently wrong with that except when it comes time to make an actual choice, it could be a difficult task because you will inevitably have to compare the different proposals on an apples-to-apples basis. And when you are dealing with engineering and construction, this is more complicated than it seems on the surface. So just because one engineer charges you less money does not mean that it will cost you less in the long run. Additionally, most condo boards must obtain three bids when hiring professional services. And like in every business, all proposals are not built the same. Some proposals leave things out on purpose, and others don't. It's always up to the buyer to ensure his interests are being protected. Hiring a lawyer should always be on the table if you deem that a proposal is too wordy, unclear, or in "legalese."

To illustrate how a cheaper engineer could wind up costing you more money, I'll begin by providing you an over-simplified example: Engineer "A" will charge you $5,000 for a set of plans for an addition to your home, and Engineer "B" will charge you $10,000. Upon examining the proposals closely, you see that the cheaper engineer excludes critical items such as meeting with the Building Department, project administration, answering contractor questions, jobsite inspections to ensure the contractors are doing things correctly, checking the contractor invoices before payment, etc. Once you add up all costs of these services that contractor "A" didn't add to his proposal, he would have handed you a bid for $15,000. There are many other considerations one should keep in mind when looking to hire an engineer, such as:

- Does the engineer have Errors and Omissions insurance?

- Is the engineer experienced enough and have a list of past clients he can show you?

- Does he have a staff who can do the work if the main person is unavailable?

- Is the person licensed?

- Does the person have any past complaints levied against them at the state's engineering board?

You can see that just calling some engineers and obtaining a few proposals could become a complicated endeavor if you want to drastically increase the chances of having a successful project with minimal issues. There is, however, a structured way to find out who the best engineer is for the job. It's through the proper use of the RFP, or a "Request for a Proposal." With a Request for Proposal, you are the one who will tell the engineers what the scope of the work entails, how you want their proposals written, the minimum requirements needed, the time and date that you expect their proposals, among other key items.

Parts of the RFP (Request for Proposal) explained

The RFP mainly comprises six parts:

1. Background

2. Requirements

3. Fee and Payment terms

4. References

5. Contacts

6. Due Date and Time

Background: The Background is merely giving a little bit of the backstory to the bidding engineer so that they are in tune with the realities behind the project and thus can provide a more realistic proposal given your specific needs. A good engineer will want to know the reasons behind why these inspections or renovations are being done, such as, "It was an overdue beautification project that all the owners wanted," or, "The Building Department issued a citation because the work poses a threat the safety of the residents."

Requirements: This section is where the engineer will understand exactly what is expected of them and what they are to include (and not include) in their proposal. The more information you provide the engineer about the scope of work and your expectations, the more precise your proposals will be. There are other requirements that are extremely important such as expecting the engineer to have "Errors and Omissions Insurance" or what we in the industry call E&O insurance. E&O insurance is a kind of specialized liability protection against losses not covered by traditional liability insurance. It protects the engineer from claims if you (or your condominium) sue for negligent acts, errors, or omissions committed during business activities that result in a financial loss. Engineers are human and at times make mistakes on plans, and unfortunately, these mistakes translate to financial losses for the owners. This type of insurance can come in handy during difficult times on the project. If your engineer does not have E&O Insurance, you can ask them why, since most competent and established firms have an active E&O insurance policy. I am not saying that engineers without E&O Insurance are bad engineers, but it raises a red flag if you are in the market for an established, trustworthy firm. You can ask to see their "E&O Insurance Policy Binder" to prove they possess it. The typical coverage for a small-to-medium engineering firm is $1,000,000 per occurrence.

Fee and Payment Terms: Since engineering and construction projects can be very complicated, it thus follows that charging for these services could also be convoluted. Many engineers charge on a lump-sum basis, but some projects charge based on hourly rates, percentage of completion, or other types of payments. In addition, some engineers charge for reimbursable costs such as mailings, plan reproductions, and travel time. Furthermore, if an incompetent contractor is hired, this makes the engineer's life more difficult, thus spending more time on the project than previously estimated. There are many reasons why an engineer will include hourly rates (in addition to lump-sum items) in his proposal, and each engineer will have his way of adding these fees and payment terms into their proposal.

At the end of the day, it will be up to the owner to sift through the proposals and figure out a way to compare fees and payment terms on an apples-to-apples basis. However, if you let the engineers know your expectations up front, your work is drastically simplified. This is where the RFP comes in handy. You are the one to tell your bidding engineers up front how they should structure their fees so you can easily compare the different bids to one another.

References: Although references are not a complete guarantee of success, they are a great way to know a little more about your engineer. It will suffice to ask your bidding engineer to provide you with two names and numbers of past clients that have performed a similar scope of work in the past. Granted, engineers (as any other business person) will only provide references of people that they have satisfied in their work, so many people take the reference stamp of approval with a grain of salt.

Contacts: Your bidders must know who to send their bids to. The person who receives the bids must be trustworthy because the receipt of these bids is susceptible to tampering and fraud. I have always found that the most fool-proof way to accept bids is by asking the bidders to submit their RFPs in sealed envelopes to only be opened when all those in charge are present (such as a condominium board meeting). The contact information should be concise, clear, and detailed so that there are no misunderstandings about to whom and where the proposals are to be sent.

Due Date and Time. Having done hundreds of RFPs (both creating the RFP as well as replying to them), this is the part that the vast majority of the bidders look at first because they must make a snap decision on whether they will invest their time to read, prepare for, understand, and reply to it. Therefore, this part must be underlined or in bold print. If too little time is allotted to the task, you may find it challenging to find an engineer to fulfill your timing requirements. Typically, you should give your engineers three weeks (from the time you send them the RFP) to provide a proposal for a smaller project and a maximum of 6 weeks for a larger, more complicated project. You should also provide a time frame for them to call or email with any questions.

In conclusion, the RFP is a powerful tool to obtain proposals that will be easy to analyze your bids on an apples-to-apples basis and save you, the owner, time. Furthermore, all the bidding engineers will be on the same page and bid on the same written scope of work, and therefore the chances of misunderstandings occurring will be kept at a minimum. Hopefully, you have reviewed the bids and have chosen the best engineer following the basic guidelines in this book. Now that you have the engineer, you have paved a path towards a successful project.

Please note that if you are searching for an engineer to perform your concrete repair plans and specifications, Appendix A provides more detailed information on searching for and finding your engineer. Appendix A also provides a very simplified step-by-step process for how concrete repairs at your building will be performed.

G. BATISTA
ENGINEERING&
CONSTRUCTION

CPSIA information can be obtained
at www.ICGtesting.com
Printed in the USA
LVHW081208230622
721938LV00010B/462